Easy Learning

Louis Cornish

KS3 Maths Workbook

Levels 5-8

Keith Gordon

About this book

This book has been written to help you prepare for your Key Stage 3 Maths Test at the end of Year 9. It contains all the practice you need to do well in the two written papers and the mental test.

The book is divided into four sections which correspond to the four areas of assessment (Attainment Targets) in the National Curriculum. Each double page contains SAT-style questions on a specific topic. At the back of the book, there are two practice papers (one with calculator allowed), a mental test and a revision checklist.

The questions have been given approximate National Curriculum levels to show you what level the question is. You still need to practise answering the lower level questions to check that you fully understand the topic, even if you are working at a higher level.

Use the space on the page to do your working out and put your answer on the answer line provided. If you need more space for your working, use an extra sheet of paper.

How to check your answers

You can check your answers for FREE by visiting **www.collinseducation.com/easylearning** where full mark and level guidance is also given in an easy-to-download format.

Revision and practice

Each double page in this book is specifically matched to a double page in Collins *Easy Learning KS3 Maths Revision Levels 5–8*. You can revise the topic in the revision book and then test yourself by answering the questions in this workbook.

Published by Collins
An imprint of HarperCollins*Publishers*
77 – 85 Fulham Palace Road
Hammersmith
London W6 8JB

Browse the complete Collins catalogue at
www.collins.co.uk

© HarperCollins*Publishers* Limited 2006

10 9 8 7 6 5 4 3 2

ISBN-13 978-0-00-723356-4
ISBN-10 0-00-723356-6

Keith Gordon asserts his moral right to be identified as the author of this work.

British Library Cataloguing in Publication Data
A Catalogue record for this publication is available from the British Library

Written by Keith Gordon
Edited by Ros Davies and Chris Davies
Design by Andy Summers, Planet Creative Ltd
Illustrations by Kathy Baxendale, Jerry Fowler, David Whittle, Tony Wilkins
Printed and bound in Malaysia by Imago

Contents

NUMBER

Multiplying and dividing decimals

1 The diagram shows how to change metres into millimetres.

$$\text{Number of metres} \xrightarrow{\quad\times 10^2\quad} \text{Number of centimetres} \xrightarrow{\quad\times 10\quad} \text{Number of millimetres}$$

a Change 3.4 metres into millimetres.

_____

b Change 74 millimetres into metres.

_____

2 Work out the following.

a $5.43 \times 10 =$ _____

b $0.347 \times 10^2 =$ _____

c $6.72 \div 10 =$ _____

d $80.7 \div 10^3 =$ _____

3 Fill in the missing numbers.

a $5 \div 10 =$ _____

b _____ $\times 10^2 = 230$

c $0.6 \div 10^2 =$ _____

d $0.6 \times$ _____ $= 60$

4 Will spends £17.10 each week in bus fares.

a How much would he spend on bus fares in 4 weeks?

b How much would he save with a monthly pass that costs £56.50?

5 Rhona bought 3 CDs and 5 DVDs.
How much does she pay altogether?

£15.95

£8.99

_____

6 Jamal buys 5 new tyres for his car.
The total bill is £325.
How much was each tyre?

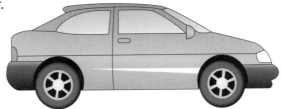

_____

1 mark

7 Work out the following.

a 4.6 x 7 =

b 35.4 ÷ 6 =

_____

c 8 x 5.2 =

d 58.1 ÷ 7 =

_____

_____

4 marks

8 Six people buy a meal in a restaurant and
the bill comes to £256.80.

If they share the cost equally how much
does each person pay?

_____

1 mark

9 Which is the larger amount:
one-fifth of £46 or one-eighth of £73?

_____

1 mark

NUMBER

Long multiplication and division

1 Work out the following.

  a 27 x 32 _____  2 marks

  b 36 x 217 _____ 2 marks

  c 952 ÷ 28 _____ 2 marks

  d 994 ÷ 14 _____ 2 marks

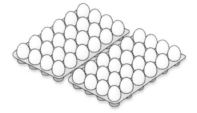

2 a Eggs are delivered in trays of 48.
How many eggs will be in 17 trays?

_____ 2 marks

  b A restaurant orders 1000 eggs.

   i How many full trays will they need?

_____ 2 marks

   ii How many eggs will be in the last tray?

_____ 2 marks

3 One bus carries 52 passengers.
  a How many passengers could be
  carried on 23 buses?

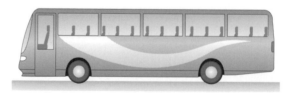

_____ 2 marks

  b A school is taking 950 students to a theme park at the end of term.
  How many buses will they need to hire?

_____ 2 marks

4 Maths textbooks are sold in packs of 15.

   a A school orders 24 packs.

     How many books are there in 24 packs?

     _____ **2 marks**

   b Another school has 272 students in Year 9.

     i How many packs will the school need to order to get a maths
       textbook for each student?

       _____ **2 marks**

     ii Will the school have enough spare textbooks to give one to each
       of the 11 maths teachers?

       Show your working. _____ **1 mark**

5 a Tickets to an orchestral concert in a school hall are £42 each.
     350 people attended the concert.
     The orchestra charged £12 500 for playing the concert.
     How much money did the school make?

     _____ **2 marks**

   b There were 28 members of the orchestra and one conductor.
     Each member of the orchestra was paid £400.
     The rest of the money was paid to the conductor.
     How much money did the conductor get?

     _____ **2 marks**

   c The 350 people sat in rows of 24 seats.
     How many rows of seats were needed?

     _____ **1 mark**

6 What is the remainder when 617 is divided by 23?

     _____ **1 mark**

7 How many boxes of cakes, each holding 12 cakes, will be needed
   to give 120 guests at a garden party three cakes each?

     _____ **1 mark**

1 Look at the following list of numbers.

−7, −6, −2, −1, 0, 2, 4, 8

   a What is the total of all eight numbers in the list?

   _____

1 mark

   b Choose three different numbers from the list that have the lowest total.

   _____

1 mark

   c Choose two numbers from the list so that the product is as low as possible.

   _____

1 mark

2 The diagram shows how to change °C into °F.

Temperature (°C) → ÷ 5 → x 9 → + 32 → Temperature (°F)

   a Change 20 °C into °F. _____ **1 mark**

   b Change −40 °C into °F. _____ **1 mark**

   c Change −4 °F into °C. _____ **1 mark**

3 Using = (equals), < (less than) or > (greater than), put the correct sign between each number sentence. The first one has been done for you.

   a 5 − 6 < 6 − 5   **b** −9 _____ −3

   c +7 − −8 _____ +8 − −7   **d** 4 x −2 _____ −4 x 2   **3 marks**

4 Work out the following.

   a −8 + 3 − 6 _____   **b** −3 x −2 + 5 _____

   c −32 ÷ +8 _____   **d** (−4 − 3) x −6 _____   **4 marks**

5 Fill in two **negative** numbers to make the following true.

a ☐ + ☐ = [−5]

b ☐ − ☐ = [−5]

6 Write the missing numbers on the number lines.

a

+27

☐ → 13

b

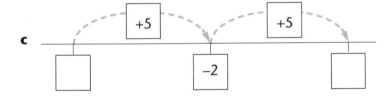

☐

−15 → −8

c

+5   +5

☐   −2   ☐

7 a Two numbers multiply together to make +12 and add together
to make −8. What are the two numbers?

_____

b 7 squared is 49. The square of another number is also 49.
What is the other number?

_____

8 Look at the following number machine.

Input ──────→ ⟩ × 2 ⟩ ──────→ ⟩ + 5 ⟩ Output ──────→

a If the input is −3 what is the output?   _____

b If the output is −3 what is the input?   _____

Adding and subtracting fractions

1 **a** How many sixths are there in $2\frac{5}{6}$? _____ 　1 mark

 　b How many sixths are there in $1\frac{2}{3}$? _____ 　1 mark

2 **a** Convert $\frac{15}{4}$ to a mixed number. _____ 　1 mark

 　b Convert $2\frac{6}{7}$ to a top-heavy fraction. _____ 　1 mark

3 Work out the following.

 　a $\frac{1}{3} + \frac{2}{5}$ _____ 　2 marks

 　b $\frac{3}{5} - \frac{1}{4}$ _____ 　2 marks

 　c $\frac{3}{8} + \frac{3}{5}$ _____ 　2 marks

 　d $\frac{7}{8} - \frac{2}{3}$ _____ 　2 marks

4 Work out the following.

 　a $2\frac{1}{4} + 3\frac{1}{5}$ _____ 　2 marks

 　b $3\frac{2}{5} + 1\frac{1}{8}$ _____ 　2 marks

 　c $4\frac{1}{5} - 3\frac{3}{4}$ _____ 　2 marks

 　d $2\frac{3}{4} - 1\frac{1}{3}$ _____ 　2 marks

5 The diagram shows a grey rectangle that is 8 cm by 6 cm. Two black squares, one 4 cm by 4 cm and the other 2 cm by 2 cm, are drawn inside it.

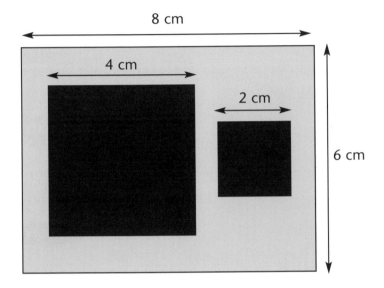

a What fraction of the rectangle is shaded black?

_____ **2 marks**

b What fraction of the rectangle is shaded grey?

_____ **2 marks**

6 Work out the following.

a $\left(\frac{2}{5}\right)^2$ _____ **1 mark**

b $\sqrt{\frac{4}{49}}$ _____ **1 mark**

c $\sqrt{\frac{4}{9}} \times \left(\frac{3}{5}\right)^2$ _____ **2 marks**

Multiplying and dividing fractions

1 What is $\frac{3}{4} \times \frac{1}{6}$ in its simplest form?

2 Work out $\frac{1}{8} \div \frac{5}{6}$. Give the answer in its simplest form.

3 How many $\frac{1}{5}$ are in $2\frac{2}{5}$?

4 a Convert $\frac{21}{5}$ to a mixed number.

   b Convert $3\frac{1}{6}$ to a top-heavy fraction.

5 Work out the following.

   a $\frac{1}{9} \times \frac{3}{5}$

   b $\frac{3}{10} \div \frac{6}{25}$

   c $\frac{3}{5} \times \frac{10}{21}$

   d $\frac{4}{9} \div \frac{2}{3}$

6 Work out the following.

   a $2\frac{1}{4} \times 1\frac{1}{5}$

   b $2\frac{3}{4} \div 4\frac{1}{8}$

   c $3\frac{2}{3} \times 2\frac{1}{4}$

   d $1\frac{7}{8} \div 2\frac{1}{12}$

7 Work out the area of this rectangle.

$1\frac{1}{5}$ cm

$2\frac{7}{8}$ cm

_____ cm²

8 Work out the areas of these triangles.

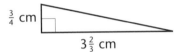

$\frac{3}{4}$ cm

$3\frac{2}{3}$ cm

a _____ cm²

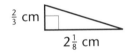

$\frac{2}{3}$ cm

$2\frac{1}{8}$ cm

b _____ cm²

9 How many $2\frac{1}{5}$ metre strips of tape can be cut from a roll of tape that is **66** metres long?

_____

10 This rectangle has an area of **8** cm².
Work out the width.

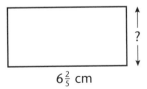

?

$6\frac{2}{5}$ cm

_____ cm

1 Alex asked 50 children what their favourite lunch was.

Lunch	Boys	Girls
Pizza	4	3
Burgers	6	6
Fish cakes	2	3
Sausages	7	6
Salad	1	12
Total	20	30

a What percentage of the children surveyed preferred pizza?

_____

1 mark

b Which lunch did 10% of the boys prefer? _____

1 mark

c Which lunch did 40% of the girls prefer? _____

1 mark

d Alex said, 'My survey shows that burgers are just as popular with girls as with boys.' Explain why Alex is wrong.

_____

_____

1 mark

e Which lunch is equally popular with boys and girls? _____

1 mark

2 A clothes shop is having a sale.
All clothes are reduced by 20%.

a What is the sale price of a jacket normally priced at £60?

_____

1 mark

b What is the sale price of a shirt normally priced at £32?

_____

1 mark

c On the last day of the sale, the **sale price** is reduced by a further 10%.
Which of the following is the last day price of a pair of boots normally priced at £100? Tick the correct answer.

☐ £80   ☐ £70   ☐ £72   ☐ £90

1 mark

3 The table shows the 2005 population of each of the world's continents.

Continent	Population (in millions)
Australasia	33
Africa	841
Asia	3825
Europe	735
North America	492
South America	379
World total	6305

a Which continent had about 6% of the world's population in 2005?

_____ **1 mark**

b In 2005, what percentage of the world's population was living in Africa?

_____ **2 marks**

4 The pie chart shows how a farmer uses his land.
The angle for fallow land is 45°.

a What percentage of the farm is fallow land?

_____ **1 mark**

b 330 acres are used for crops. What is the total acreage of the farm?

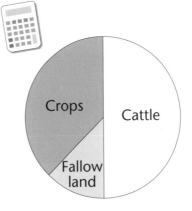

_____ **2 marks**

c Next year the farmer plans to decrease the acreage for cattle by $33\frac{1}{3}$ % and increase the amount for crops by $33\frac{1}{3}$%.
Tick the statement that is true.

☐ The amount of fallow land will stay the same.

☐ The amount of fallow land will increase.

☐ The amount of fallow land will decrease.

☐ You cannot tell how the amount of fallow land will change.

1 mark

1 In 2004, 320 passengers on average used the train line between Barnsley and Huddersfield each weekday.

In 2005, 464 passengers on average used the same train.

What percentage increase is this?

_____ %   **2 marks**

2 A standard box of cereal contains 900 g of cereal.

It is recommended that one serving is 60 grams.

a How many servings will you get from a standard box?

_____   **1 mark**

b A special offer box contains 20% more cereal than a standard box.

How many servings will you get from this box?

_____   **1 mark**

3 a What percentage of 25 is 4?

_____ %   **1 mark**

b What percentage is 6 of 48?

_____ %   **1 mark**

4 Robert got the following marks for a series of tests.

Put them in percentage order, with the smallest percentage first.

6 out of 10; 13 out of 20; 40 out of 64; 32 out of 50.

_____   **2 marks**

5 After pruning, a conifer was decreased in height from 4 m 40 cm to 3 m 74 cm.

What percentage decrease is this?

_____%   **2 marks**

6 A Petri dish contains 35 000 bacteria.

A disinfectant is added that kills 12% of the bacteria each minute.

How many bacteria will there be after 10 minutes?

_____   **2 marks**

7 An ant colony increases by 6% per day.

Initially there are 1000 ants.

   a How many will there be after a week?

   b After a week the colony is treated with an insecticide that decreases the population by 6% per day.

     How many ants will there be after a further week?

8 After a 12% reduction the price of a TV is £308.

What was the original price of the TV?

£_____

9 After treating with fertilizer the average weight of John's tomatoes increased by 15% to 92 grams.

What was the average weight before the treatment?

_____ g

10 This rectangle has an area of 24 cm².

The length increases by 10%.

The width increases by 20%.

What is the percentage increase of the area?

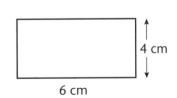

4 cm

6 cm

_____ %

1 **a** Write the ratio 6 : 9 in its simplest form. _____ 1 mark

   b Write the ratio 15 : 25 in its simplest form. _____ 1 mark

2 The ratio of two packets of cornflakes is 3 : 4

Find the mass of the larger packet. _____ 2 marks

3 Shade the diagram so that the ratio of shaded squares to unshaded squares is 1 : 3

1 mark

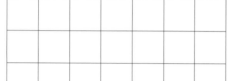

4 **a** Divide £90 in the ratio 1 : 4

_____ 2 marks

   b Divide 150 kg in the ratio 2 : 3

_____ 2 marks

5 A drink is made from cranberry juice and lemonade in the ratio 2 : 7

   a How much lemonade is needed if 50 ml of cranberry juice is used?

_____ 2 marks

   b How much cranberry juice is in 450 ml of the drink?

_____ 2 marks

6 The diagram shows a grey rectangle
8 cm by 6 cm with a black square
3 cm by 3 cm drawn inside it.

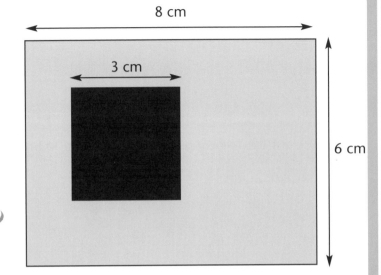

8 cm

3 cm

6 cm

a Calculate the ratio of the perimeter of
the rectangle to the perimeter of the
square. Give your answer in its
simplest form.

_____   **2 marks**

b Calculate the ratio
grey area : black area
Give your answer in its simplest form.

_____   **2 marks**

7 Fatima won £146 on the lottery.
She decided to start two bank accounts for her grandchildren, Nadia, aged 3 years old
and Naseem, aged 5.
She shared the money between the children in the ratio of their ages.

a How much did each child get in the bank?   _____   **2 marks**

b The following year she won another £146 and did the same thing with the money.

How much would each child have in the bank in total now?

_____   **2 marks**

8 A fizzy drink is sold in two sizes. The small bottle
costs 35p and the larger bottle costs 60p.

a Write down the ratio of the sizes of the bottles in
its simplest form. _____   **1 mark**

b Write down the ratio of the costs of the bottles in
its simplest form. _____   **1 mark**

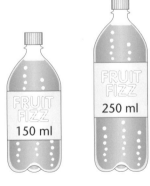

250 ml

150 ml

c Which size is the best value for money?

Explain your answer. _____

_____   **2 marks**

1 Work out the following.

  a 2^6

  _____ 1 mark

  b 3^7

  _____ 1 mark

2 Work out the following leaving the answer in index form.

  a $4^4 \times 4^3$

  _____ 1 mark

  b $5^8 \div 5^2$

  _____ 1 mark

3 Put these numbers in order of size, smallest first.

  $\sqrt[3]{64}$ 2^3 3^2 $\sqrt{25}$ 25°

  _____ 2 marks

4 Here are some number cards.

2^4 4^2 3^3 8^1 8^0

  a Which number is the largest?

  _____ 1 mark

  b Which two cards have the same value?

  _____ 1 mark

5 Some numbers are smaller than their squares.

  For example: $3 < 3^2$

  a Which number is equal to its square? _____ 1 mark

  b Give an example of a number that is greater than its square. _____ 1 mark

6 $\sqrt{30}$ lies between 5 and 6 because $5^2 = 25$ and $6^2 = 36$.

  Find two whole numbers between which the following must lie.

  a $\sqrt{15}$

  _____ 1 mark

  b $\sqrt[3]{10}$

  _____ 1 mark

7 Find values of a, b and c such that

$64 = 2^a = 4^b = 8^c$

$a = $ _____

$b = $ _____

$c = $ _____

3 marks

8 Find the values of m and n such that

$2^m \times 3^n = 108$

$m = $ _____

$n = $ _____

2 marks

9 A cube has a volume of 125 cm³.

a What is the length of the side?

_____ cm **1 mark**

b What is the surface area of the cube?

_____ cm² **1 mark**

10 Shona writes down that $\sqrt{x + y} = \sqrt{x} + \sqrt{y}$

Give an example to show that Shona is wrong.

_____ **1 mark**

11 Tony thinks that $\sqrt{x \times y} = \sqrt{x} \times \sqrt{y}$

Give an example to show that Tony is correct.

_____ **1 mark**

12 There is only one pair of numbers, a and b, which are different and for which $a^b = b^a$

What values are a and b?

_____ **1 mark**

1 Round off the following numbers to 1 significant figure.

a 46.89 _____ **b** 0.0065 _____

2 marks

2 Complete the following table.

Number	Rounded to 1 s.f.	Rounded to 2 s.f.	Rounded to 3 s.f.
5.682			
34 639			
0.09938			

9 marks

3 The width of a square tile is 150 mm, correct to the nearest millimetre.

a What is the least possible width of one tile? _____ mm

1 mark

b What is the greatest possible width of one tile? _____ mm

1 mark

c 12 tiles are placed together.

What is the least possible width of the 12 tiles? _____ mm

1 mark

4 The weight of a chocolate bar is 40 grams to 1 significant figure.

a What is the least possible weight of one chocolate bar? _____ g

1 mark

b What is the greatest possible weight of one chocolate bar? _____ g

1 mark

c Gita has four chocolate bars.

What is the greatest possible weight of Gita's chocolate bars? _____ g

1 mark

5 This table shows the percentage of nationalities on an aeroplane.

Nationality	British	American	French	German	Italian
Percentage	32.5	19.6	22.1	15.1	10.7

a Add up all the percentages. _____ %

1 mark

b Round all the percentages to the nearest whole number. _____

1 mark

c Add up the rounded values. Explain your answer. _____ %

_____

1 mark

6 Work out an approximate answer to the following.

a $\dfrac{412 \times 39}{18.3}$

_____   **1 mark**

b $\dfrac{21.8 \times 42.6}{9.25 \times 5.24}$

_____   **1 mark**

7 Use your calculator to work out the following.

$$\dfrac{2.51 \times 6.62}{\sqrt{4.84}}$$

a Write down all the digits on your calculator display.

_____   **1 mark**

b Round off your answer to 2 significant figures.

_____   **1 mark**

8 A rectangle has a length of 8 cm and a width of 6 cm, with both values measured to the nearest centimetre.

a What are the least and greatest values of the length?

least _____ cm   greatest _____ cm   **2 marks**

b What are the least and greatest values of the width?

least _____ cm   greatest _____ cm   **2 marks**

c What are the least and greatest values of the area?

least _____ cm² greatest _____ cm²   **2 marks**

9 A cube has a side of 5 cm measured to the nearest centimetre.

What is the greatest possible volume?

_____ cm³   **1 mark**

1 Write the following numbers in standard form.

  a 0.000008 _____

  1 mark

  b 67 000 000 000 _____

  1 mark

2 Complete the following table, writing the rounded numbers in standard form.

Number	Rounded to 1 s.f.	Rounded to 2 s.f.	Rounded to 3 s.f.
0.004578			
34 640 000			
0.00009638			

9 marks

3 Write the following standard form numbers as ordinary numbers.

  a 6.8×10^5 _____

  1 mark

  b 8.9×10^{-4} _____

  1 mark

  c 9.85×10^8 _____

  1 mark

4 The following numbers are not in standard form.
Write them correctly in standard form.

  a 34.5×10^6 _____

  1 mark

  b 0.7×10^5 _____

  1 mark

  c $4.2 \times 10^6 \times 5 \times 10^2$ _____

  1 mark

  d $4.2 \times 10^6 \div 5 \times 10^2$ _____

  1 mark

5 Write the following numbers in standard form.

  a 8 million _____

  1 mark

  b one thousandth _____

  1 mark

  c sixteen thousand _____

  1 mark

6 The Earth is an approximate sphere with a radius of 6400 km.

a The formula for working out the volume of a sphere is

$$V = \frac{4}{3}\pi r^3$$

Work out the volume of the Earth, giving your answer in standard form to 2 s.f.

_____ **2 marks**

b The surface area of a sphere is given by

$$A = 4\pi r^2$$

70% of the surface area of the Earth is covered by water.
Work out the area of water, giving your answer in standard form to 2 s.f.

_____ **2 marks**

7 A nanometre (nm) is 1×10^{-9} of a metre.
A hydrogen atom is 0.12 nm across.

Write this value in metres in standard form.

_____ **1 mark**

8 Computer screens are split into pixels. One screen has a resolution of 72 pixels per inch. There are 2.54 centimetres to an inch.

a Using the above information, write down the width of a pixel in centimetres. Give your answer in standard form.

_____ cm **1 mark**

b Pixels are square in shape. What is the area of an individual pixel? Give your answer in square centimetres in standard form to 3 s.f.

_____ cm² **1 mark**

c One screen is 800 pixels by 600 pixels. What is the area of the screen? Give your answer in square centimetres to 1 d.p.

_____ cm² **1 mark**

ALGEBRA Sequences

1 The table shows the counting numbers arranged in a six column grid.

	Col 1	Col 2	Col 3	Col 4	Col 5	Col 6
Row 1	1	2	3	4	5	6
Row 2	⑦	8	9	10	11	12
Row 3	13	⑭	15	16	17	18
Row 4	19	20	㉑	22	23	24

a Which column will the number 37 be in?

_____ **1 mark**

b Column 2 makes the sequence 2, 8, 14, 20, ...
What will be the 10th term of this sequence?

_____ **1 mark**

c The nth term of the numbers in the 4th column is $6n - 2$.
What is the nth term of the numbers in the 5th column?

_____ **1 mark**

d The 7 times table is circled. Row 1 does not have any numbers
in the 7 times table.

Which is the next row without a number in the 7 times table?

_____ **1 mark**

2 What is the next number in this sequence?

10, 7, 4, 1, –2, ...

_____ **1 mark**

3 A sequence has the term-to-term rule 'multiply by 2 and add 1'.
Which of these series of three terms could be in the sequence?
Tick the correct answer. (There may be more than one.)

☐ 1, 3, 5, ...

☐ 2, 5, 11, ...

☐ 10, 21, 63, ...

☐ –3, –5, –9, ...

1 mark

4 The nth term of a sequence is $2n - 1$.
Write down the first three terms in the sequence. _____

2 marks

5 Look at this series of patterns.

Pattern 1

Pattern 2

Pattern 3

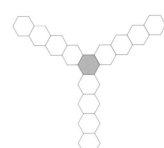

Pattern 4

a How many grey hexagons will there be in Pattern 6?

_____ **1 mark**

b What is the *n*th term of the sequence of white hexagons?

_____ **1 mark**

6 Look at this series of patterns.

Pattern 1

Pattern 2

Pattern 3

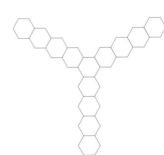

Pattern 4

What is the *n*th term of the number of hexagons in each sequence?

_____ **2 marks**

7 What is the missing term in this sequence?

3, 4, ... , 12, 19, 28, 39, 52 _____ **1 mark**

8 What is the *n*th term in this sequence?

8, 12, 16, 20, 24, ...  **2 marks**

Square numbers, primes and proof

levels 5-8

1 Write down the factors of 24. _____

2 marks

2 What is the highest common factor of 24 and 64?

_____

1 mark

3 What is the lowest common multiple of 9 and 12?

_____

1 mark

4 Which of the following is both a square number and a triangle number?
Tick the correct answer.

☐ 4   ☐ 9   ☐ 25   ☐ 36

1 mark

5 Write down a square number between 101 and 149. _____

1 mark

6 Here are 10 number cards. | 1 | 2 | 3 | 4 | 5 | 6 | 7 | 8 | 9 | 10 |

From the cards, write down

   a the square numbers _____

2 marks

   b the prime numbers _____

2 marks

   c the factors of 10 _____

1 mark

7 Circle A contains the first ten multiples of 2.
Circle B contains the first seven multiples of 3.

A

2
8
10
4
14
16
20
...
...
...
3
9
15
21

B

Write down the missing numbers
from the overlap.

_____

_____

_____

2 marks

8 Circle A contains the factors of 20.
Circle B contains the factors of 36.

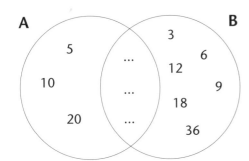

A   B   Write down the missing numbers
from the overlap.

_____

_____

_____

2 marks

9 p is a prime number, q is an even number, r is an odd number.
State whether the following expressions are:
Always even, Always odd, Could be either odd or even.

	Even	Odd	Either
a p^2	☐	☐	☐
b $p(q + r)$	☐	☐	☐
c q^2	☐	☐	☐
d pqr	☐	☐	☐

4 marks

10 n is an integer.

a Explain why $2n$ is an even number.

_____

1 mark

b Explain why $2n + 1$ is an odd number.

_____

1 mark

c Prove that the product of an even number and
an odd number is always even.

1 mark

11 Prove algebraically that the sum of three consecutive integers is a multiple of 3.

2 marks

ALGEBRA — Algebraic manipulation 1

1 If $a = -3$, $b = +4$ and $c = -5$ which of the following expressions is equal to 3?
Tick the correct answer. (There may be more than one.)

☐ $a(b + c)$ ☐ $a^2 + b^2$

☐ $ab + ac$ ☐ $(c - b) \div a$

1 mark

2 Simplify the following expressions.

  a $4(2x - 3)$ _____ **1 mark**

  b $3a \times 5a$ _____ **1 mark**

  c $3(a + 2b) + 4(2a - b)$ _____ **1 mark**

  d $5(3x + 2) - 5(2x - 3)$ _____ **1 mark**

3 William has a pile of cards.
The total number of cards is $4n + 8$.

  a William puts the cards into 2 piles.
  The number of cards in one pile is $3n + 1$.
  How many cards are in the other pile?

_____ **1 mark**

  b William puts the cards into 4 equal piles.

  How many cards are in each pile?

_____ **1 mark**

  c William counts the cards and finds he has 32 in total.
  What is the value of n?

_____ **1 mark**

4   Look at the rectangle. Write down expressions for the lengths marked **a** and **b**.

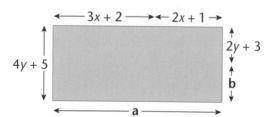

a = _____ **1 mark**

b = _____ **1 mark**

5 Here are four cards with algebraic expressions on them.

| 2(x + 1) | 3(x − 2) | 2(x − 1) | 3(x + 1) |
| Card A | Card B | Card C | Card D |

Work out the algebraic expressions formed by:

a Card A + Card B _____ **1 mark**

b Card A + Card C _____ **1 mark**

c Card B − Card C _____ **1 mark**

d Card D − Card A _____ **1 mark**

6 In these walls each brick is made by adding together the two bricks below it.

For example:

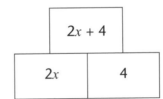

Write the missing expressions in the walls below as simply as possible.

a

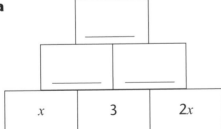

b

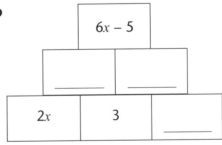

6 marks

7 Work out **a** the perimeter and **b** the area of this shape in terms of x.

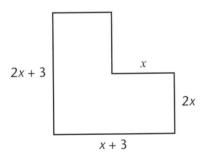

a Perimeter _____ **1 mark**

b Area _____ **1 mark**

1 Simplify the following expressions.

a $3a^2b \times 4ab$

_____ **1 mark**

b $2a^3b^2 \times 5a^2b^3$

_____ **1 mark**

c $\dfrac{6a^2b^3 \times 4a^2b}{3a^3b^2}$

_____ **1 mark**

d $\dfrac{6ab^3 \times 4a^3b}{2a \times 3b}$

_____ **1 mark**

2 Expand the following brackets.

a $(x - 3)(x + 4)$

_____ **1 mark**

b $(x + 5)(x + 3)$

_____ **1 mark**

c $(x - 1)(x - 2)$

_____ **1 mark**

d $(x + 2)(x - 4)$

_____ **1 mark**

3 a   Complete the boxes to expand $(2x + 5)(x - 2)$.

	$2x$	$+ 5$
x	$2x^2$	$+ 5x$
$- 2$	_____	_____

$(2x + 5)(x - 2) = 2x^2 + 5x$ _____

       = _____ **1 mark**

b   Expand the following brackets.

i $(2x + 3)(x + 4)$ _____ **1 mark**

ii $(3x - 1)(2x + 1)$ _____ **1 mark**

iii $(4x + 2)(3x - 4)$ _____ **1 mark**

4 The rectangle is $(n + 5)$ cm long and $(n + 3)$ cm wide.
It has been split into four smaller rectangles.

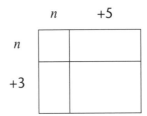

a Find the area of each small rectangle.

_____

1 mark

b Write down the expansion of $(n + 5)(n + 3)$.

_____

2 marks

5 Expand the following brackets.

a $(x - 3)(x + 3)$ _____ **1 mark**

b $(x + 5)(x - 5)$ _____ **1 mark**

c $(x - 1)(x + 1)$ _____ **1 mark**

d $(x + 4)(x - 4)$ _____ **1 mark**

6 Show that the area of this triangle is $p^2 + 6p + 5$.

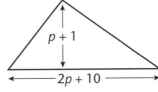

_____

2 marks

7 Work out the area of this shape in terms of x.

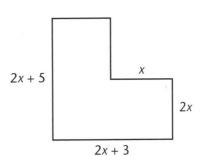

Area = _____

2 marks

ALGEBRA Factorisation

levels 7-8

1 Which of the following are **not** factors of both $12a^2b^3$ and $18ab^2$?
Tick the correct answers.

☐ $3ab$ ☐ $2a$ ☐ $18ab$ ☐ $4b$ ☐ $6ab^2$

1 mark

2 Which of the following are factors of both $15x^3y^4$ and $25xy^3$?
Tick the correct answers.

☐ $5xy$ ☐ $10x$ ☐ $5x^2y$ ☐ x^3y^4 ☐ $5xy^2$

1 mark

3 Which two of the expressions below are equivalent?

☐ $4(3a - 5)$ ☐ $3(4a - 5)$ ☐ $2(6a - 10)$ ☐ $4(a^3 - 5)$

1 mark

4 a Which of the expressions below is equivalent to the expression

$$6x^2y^2 + 24x^3y$$

$6xy(xy + 4x^2y)$ $6xy(xy^2 + 4x^2)$

$2xy(3xy + 12x^2)$ $3xy(2xy^2 + 8x^2)$ **1 mark**

b Which of the expressions below is equivalent to the expression

$$x^2 + 8x + 12$$

$(x + 3)(x + 4)$ $(x - 3)(x - 4)$

$(x + 2)(x + 6)$ $(x - 2)(x - 6)$ **1 mark**

5 Which of these expressions is the odd one out?
Explain your answer.

☐ $2y^2(y - 6)$ ☐ $2y^3 - 12y^2$ ☐ $2y(y^2 - 10)$ ☐ $2y(y^2 - 6y)$

_____

2 marks

6 a Factorise the following expression.

$$5x + 25$$

_____ **1 mark**

b Factorise the following expression as fully as possible.

$$12x^3 - 4x^2$$

_____ **1 mark**

7 Factorise the following expressions.

a $3a^2b + 4ab$ _____ **1 mark**

b $12a^3b^2 + 4a^2b^3$ _____ **1 mark**

c $6a^2b^3 + 4a^2b$ _____ **1 mark**

d $6a^2b^3 + 4a^3b^2$ _____ **1 mark**

8 Complete the following factorisations.

a $x^2 - x - 12 = (x - $ _____ $)(x + 3)$ **1 mark**

b $x^2 - 8x + 15 = (x - 5)(x$ _____ $)$ **1 mark**

c $x^2 + 3x + 2 = (x + $ _____ $)(x + $ _____ $)$ **1 mark**

d $x^2 + 2x - 24 = (x + $ _____ $)(x - $ _____ $)$ **1 mark**

9 a Use the diagram to work out the length and the width of the rectangle.

	length	
n^2	$2n$	
$5n$	10	

width

_____ **1 mark**

b Factorise $x^2 + 3x - 4$.

_____ **1 mark**

Formulae

1 The flow diagram shows a formula.

```
( Input ) — [ Multiply by 3 ] — [ Add 2 ] — ( Output )
```

Which of the following pairs of inputs and outputs work for this formula?
Tick the correct answer. (There may be more than one.)

☐ input 3, output 15   ☐ input 5, output 17

☐ input 1, output 5   ☐ input −2, output −8   **1 mark**

2 Tim is thinking of a number.

*I think of a number.
I double it and add 7.
The answer is 12.*

What was the number Tim thought of? _____   **1 mark**

3
```
( Input ) — [ Multiply by 4 ] — [ Add 1 ] — ( Output )
```

a What is the output for this flow diagram if the input is 5? _____   **1 mark**

b What is the input for this flow diagram if the output is 5? _____   **1 mark**

4
```
( x ) — [ − 2 ] — [ x 3 ] — ( Output )
```

What formula will be the output from this flow diagram? _____   **1 mark**

5 In a sale the prices are reduced by 20%.
This flow diagram shows how to work out the sale price.

```
( Original price ) — x 0.8 — ( Sale price )
```

a What is the sale price of an item with an original price of £20?

_____   **1 mark**

b What is the original price of an item with a sale price of £32?

_____   **1 mark**

6 A formula connecting three variables x, y and z is $x = y(8 - z)^2$.

   a Work out the value of y when $x = 10$ and $z = 3$. _____ **1 mark**

   b Work out the **values** of z when $x = 16$ and $y = 4$. _____ **2 marks**

7 The following two equations $v = u + at$ and $v^2 = u^2 + 2as$, connect

        s, distance in metres

        u, initial speed in metres per second

        v, final speed in metres per second

        a, acceleration in metres per second squared

        t, time of journey.

For a particular journey, $v = 25$ m/s, $u = 10$ m/s, $t = 2$ seconds.

Use the equations to find s, the distance travelled.

_____ **2 marks**

8 The shape shown consists of two cylinders fixed together.
The larger cylinder has a radius of a cm and a height of b cm.
The smaller cylinder has a radius of c cm and a height of a cm.
The volume and surface area of the shape are given by the formulae

      $V = \pi a(ab + c^2)$

      $A = 2\pi a(a + b + c)$

   a Work out the volume and area if $a = 10$ cm, $b = 20$ cm and $c = 6$ cm.
      Leave your answers in terms of π.

                     Volume = _____

                     Area   = _____ **2 marks**

   b Work out the volume and area if $a = 5.6$ cm,
      $b = 12.2$ cm and $c = 4.8$ cm.

      Give your answers to 3 significant figures.

                     Volume = _____

                     Area   = _____ **2 marks**

1 Some rectangular tiles are placed on a coordinate grid.

On the first tile the corner marked with a square has the coordinate (2, 2) and the corner marked with a triangle has the coordinate (0, 1).

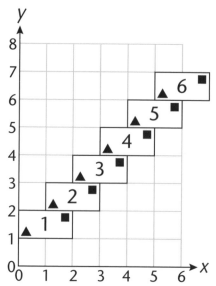

a What are the coordinates of the corner with a square on tile 6?

_____

1 mark

b What are the coordinates of the corner with a triangle on tile 7?

_____

1 mark

c What are the coordinates of the corner with a square on tile 20?

_____

1 mark

d What are the coordinates of the corner with a triangle on tile 21?

_____

1 mark

2 The equation of a line is $y + x = 8$.
Which of the following points could lie on the line?
Tick the correct answer. (There could be more than one.)

☐ (−2, −6)   ☐ (0, 8)   ☐ (−2, 10)   ☐ (10, −2)

1 mark

3 At what point do the lines $y = 3$ and $x = 2$ intersect? _____

1 mark

4 Which of these lines passes through the point (−3, 5)?
Tick the correct answer. (There could be more than one.)

☐ $x + y = 8$ ☐ $y = 5$

☐ $x + y = 2$ ☐ $x = -3$

1 mark

5 What are the equations of the lines a, b, c, d?

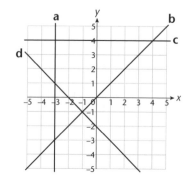

a _____

b _____

c _____

d _____

4 marks

6 A, B and C are three corners of a triangle.

  a What is the equation of the line

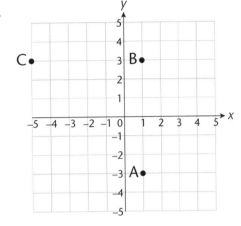

  i AB _____

1 mark

  ii BC _____

1 mark

  iii AC _____

1 mark

  b What is the area of the triangle ABC?

  _____

1 mark

7 What is the equation of the line shown?
Tick the correct answer.

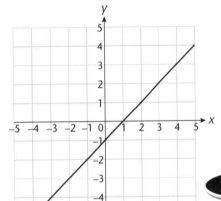

☐ $y = -1$

☐ $y = x - 1$

☐ $x = 1$

☐ $x + y = 1$

1 mark

8 A is the point (2, 5). B is the point (−3, −5).
Which of the following is the graph of the
straight line through A and B?
Tick the correct answer.

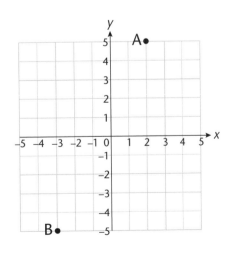

☐ $y = 2x - 1$

☐ $y = x + 3$

☐ $y = 2x + 1$

☐ $y = x - 2$

1 mark

1 The equations of four lines are

$y = 2x + 1$ $y = 2x - 3$ $y = 3x - 2$ $y = 4x + 1$

a Which two lines are parallel?

_____

1 mark

b Which two lines pass through the same point on the y-axis?

_____

1 mark

2 Match the lines on the graph with the equations.

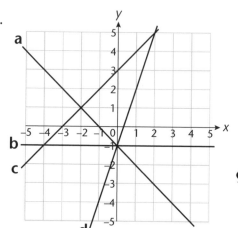

$y = x + 3$ matches line _____

$y = 3x - 1$ matches line _____

$x + y = -1$ matches line _____

$y = -1$ matches line _____

4 marks

3 The equation of a line is $y = 3x - 1$.
Which of the following points could lie on the line?
Tick the correct answer. (There could be more than one.)

☐ (2, 7)   ☐ (3, 8)   ☐ (−2, −7)   ☐ (−3, 10)

1 mark

4 The solid line on the graph is $y = 2x + 5$.
What is the equation of the line parallel to this line that passes through (0, −2)?

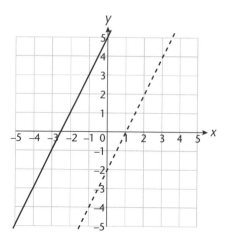

_____

1 mark

5 On the grid draw the graphs of

a $y = 3x + 1$

b $y = 2x - 3$

c $y = \frac{x}{2} + 3$

d $y = x - 4$

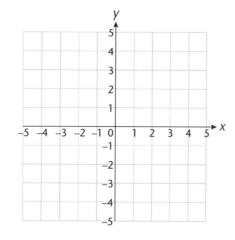

4 marks

6 Jenny does a parachute jump. Which graph shows the height against time?

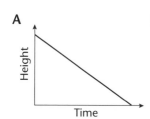 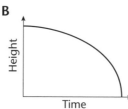 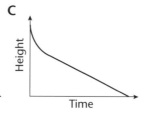 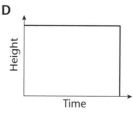

_____

1 mark

7 Mr Stead does a 5 kilometre walk that takes him 50 minutes.

The distance–time graph shows his progress.

a What is his average speed for the whole walk in kilometres per hour?

_____

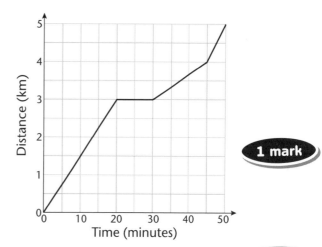

1 mark

b At one point Mr Stead took a rest.

i How many kilometres had he walked by the time he took a rest?

_____

1 mark

ii How long did he rest for?

_____

1 mark

c Mr Stead ran the last kilometre.

i How long did he take to run the last kilometre?

_____

1 mark

ii What was his average speed for the last kilometre?

_____

1 mark

1 I think of a number. Add three to it. Divide the result by 5 and I get an answer of 6. What number did I think of?

_____ **1 mark**

2 Solve the equation $2x - 7 = 20$

_____ **1 mark**

3 Solve these equations.

a $\dfrac{x-2}{3} = 7$

_____ **1 mark**

b $\dfrac{x}{3} - 2 = 7$

_____ **1 mark**

4 Solve these equations.

a $3x - 8 = 7$

_____ **1 mark**

b $\dfrac{x+3}{8} = 3$

_____ **1 mark**

5 Solve these equations.

a $\dfrac{x+3}{5} = 6$

_____ **1 mark**

b $\dfrac{x}{5} + 3 = 6$

_____ **1 mark**

c $x + \dfrac{3}{5} = 6$

_____ **1 mark**

d $5x - 3 = 6$

_____ **1 mark**

6 Solve these equations.

a $\dfrac{x}{6} = \dfrac{7}{4}$

_____ **1 mark**

b $\dfrac{x}{4} = \dfrac{9}{2}$

_____ **1 mark**

c $\dfrac{5}{x} = \dfrac{2}{7}$

_____ **1 mark**

d $\dfrac{9}{2} = \dfrac{15}{x}$

_____ **1 mark**

7 Solve these equations.

a $\dfrac{x}{6} = \dfrac{7}{3}$

_____ **1 mark**

b $\dfrac{x + 3}{4} = \dfrac{1}{2}$

_____ **1 mark**

8 Complete the following statements to solve

$$\dfrac{2x - 5}{2} = \dfrac{x - 4}{4}$$

$(2x - 5) \times 4 = (x - 4) \times$ _____

$8x - 20 =$ _____

$8x -$ _____ $= -8 +$ _____

$6x = 12$

$6x \div 6 = 12 \div$ _____

$x =$ _____   **2 marks**

1 Solve the equation $x - 7 = 2x + 3$ _____ **1 mark**

2 Solve the equation $5x - 8 = 10 + 2x$ _____ **1 mark**

3 Solve these equations.

a $\dfrac{x + 2}{5} = 6 + x$

_____ **1 mark**

b $\dfrac{x}{5} + 5 = 3 + x$

_____ **1 mark**

c $x + \dfrac{3}{5} = 6 - x$

_____ **1 mark**

d $5x - 3 = 6 + x$

_____ **1 mark**

4 The following diagram shows a rectangle.

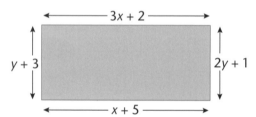

a Find the value of x.

_____ **1 mark**

b Find the value of y.

_____ **1 mark**

5 The diagrams show some bricks. The bricks on the bottom row add up to the value or expression in the top row.

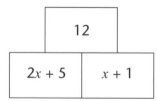

a Find the value of x. _____ **1 mark**

b Find the value of y. _____ **1 mark**

6 What inequalities are represented by the following?

a

b

7 Solve this inequality $2x - 7 < 21$

8 Solve these inequalities.

a $3x + 8 \geq 20$

b $3x - 8 > 19$

9 Solve these inequalities.

a $4(x - 1) > 6$

b $4(x + 3) \leq 12$

Trial and improvement

1 What is the value of 4^3? _____  1 mark

2 Estimate the value of 3.1^3. _____ 1 mark

3 Estimate the value of $2.7^3 + 3 \times 2.7$. _____ 1 mark

4 What is the value of $2^3 + 3 \times 2$? _____ 1 mark

5 What is the value of $3.2^3 - 2 \times 3.2$? _____ 1 mark

6 A rectangle has sides of x cm and $x + 3$ cm. It has an area of 40 cm².

Which of the following must be true?

Tick the correct answer. (There may be more than one.)

a ☐ $x(x + 3) = 40$ **b** ☐ The sides are 2 cm and 20 cm

c ☐ The sides are 5 cm and 8 cm   **d** ☐ The perimeter is 26 cm   1 mark

7 Complete the table to find a solution to the equation:
$x^3 = 100$

Give your answer to 1 decimal place.

x	x^3	Comment
4	64	Too low
5	125	Too high

$x =$ _____   3 marks

8 Complete the table to find a solution to the equation:

$x^3 + 3x = 20$

Give your answer to 1 decimal place.

x	$x^3 + 3x$	Comment
2	14	Too low

$x =$ _____

 3 marks

9 A rectangle has sides of x cm and $x + 2$ cm. It has an area of 16.64 cm².

a Explain why $x^2 + 2x = 16.64$

_____

_____

 **1 mark**

b Complete the table to find the value of x.

x	$x^2 + 2x$	Comment
2	8	Too low

$x =$ _____

 2 marks

1 Which of the following equations do the values $x = 2$ and $y = 3$ satisfy?
Tick the correct answer. (There may be more than one.)

Equation 1　$y = 2x + 1$ ☐　　Equation 2　$y = 2x - 1$ ☐

Equation 3　$2y + x = 8$ ☐　　Equation 4　$2y - x = 1$ ☐

1 mark

2 a Show that if $y = 2x + 3$ and $2y + x = 11$ then $5x + 6 = 11$

1 mark

b Solve the equation $5x + 6 = 11$

1 mark

c Find the values of x and y that satisfy these simultaneous equations.
$y = 2x + 3$ and $2y + x = 11$

$x =$ _____

$y =$ _____

1 mark

3 Both of these rectangles have a perimeter of 20 cm.

a Show that　$x + y = 4$
and　　　$2x + 3y = 10$

$3y + 1$

$2x - 1$

$3y - 2$

$3x$

2 marks

b Solve the simultaneous equations to find the values of x and y.

$x =$ _____

$y =$ _____

2 marks

4 Solve these simultaneous equations.
$$y = 2x - 1$$
$$4y = 6x + 2$$

$x =$ _____

$y =$ _____

2 marks

5 One cup of tea and a sticky bun cost £1.20.
Three teas and two sticky buns cost £3.10.

   a What is the cost of one tea?

   _____  **1 mark**

   b What is the cost of a sticky bun?

   _____ **1 mark**

6 The diagram shows an isosceles triangle.
The perimeter of the triangle is 20 cm.

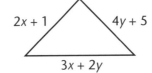

   a Show that $x - 2y = 2$

2 marks

   b Show that $5x + 6y = 14$

2 marks

   c Solve the simultaneous equations $x - 2y = 2$ and $5x + 6y = 14$.

$x =$ _____

$y =$ _____ **2 marks**

7 Two families visit the cinema.
The Watsons buy 2 adult tickets and 2 children's tickets for £14.00.
The Cricks buy 3 adult tickets and 1 child ticket for £16.00.
Let x be the cost of an adult ticket and y be the cost of a child ticket.

   a Set up two simultaneous equations using the information above.

_____ **2 marks**

   b Solve the simultaneous equations to find the cost of an adult and a child ticket.

Adult $x =$ _____

Child $y =$ _____ **2 marks**

SHAPE, SPACE AND MEASURES

Bearings

1 Fill in the missing bearings on this diagram.

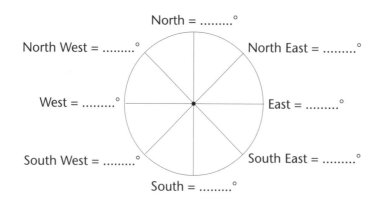

North = ...°

North West = ...°   North East = ...°

West = ...°   East = ...°

South West = ...°   South East = ...°

South = ...°

8 marks

2 From the point *O* draw the positions of the points *A, B, C,* and *D* that lie on the circle and have bearings of

A 080°; *B* 120°; *C* 220°; *D* 300°

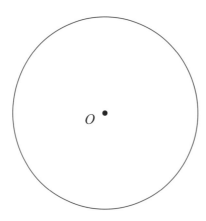

O

4 marks

3 Estimate the bearings of each of these lines.

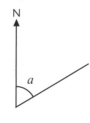

N

a

N

b

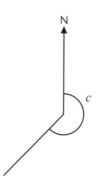

N

c

a = _____   *b* = _____   *c* = _____

3 marks

4 Measure **a** the actual distance and **b** the bearing of A, B and C from O in the diagram below.

Scale 1 cm : 2 km

C.

O

• A

B •

6 marks

5 From the point O draw the following points.

a A which is 5 cm on a bearing of 065° from O

b B which is 4 cm on a bearing of 155° from O

c C which is 6 cm on a bearing of 265° from O

O

6 marks

Angle facts

1 *PQR* is an isosceles triangle. Calculate the value of angle *g*.

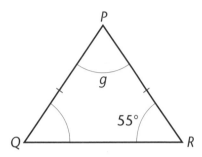

_____ ° **1 mark**

2 Calculate the size of angle *x*.

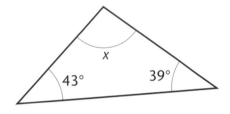

_____ ° **1 mark**

3 Calculate the size of angle *y*.

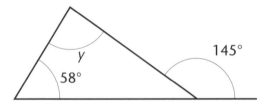

_____ ° **1 mark**

4 Calculate the size of angle *z*.

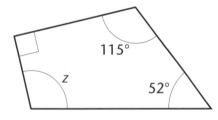

_____ ° **1 mark**

5 *ABC* is a right-angled triangle. *ACD* is an isosceles triangle.
Angle *BAC* = 35°. Angle *CAD* = 40°.

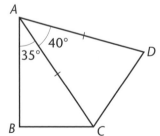

   a Find angle *CDA*.

_____ ° **1 mark**

   b Find angle *BCD*.

_____ ° **1 mark**

6 Using the diagram explain why
$z = x + y$

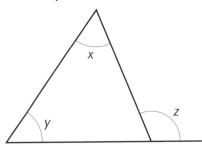

_____

_____

_____

2 marks

7 The diagram shows a rectangle *ABEF* inside a regular octagon *ABCDEFGH*.

a What shape is the quadrilateral *BCDE*?

_____

1 mark

b What is value of the angle *EBC*?

_____°

1 mark

8 The diagram shows an equilateral triangle *ABC* and a regular pentagon *BCDEF*.

Work out the value of the angle *FBA*.

_____°

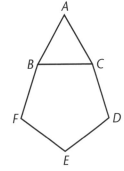

1 mark

9 This star is constructed on a regular pentagon.

a Write down the value of angle *a*.

_____

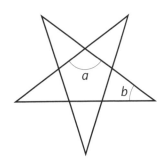

1 mark

b Write down the value of angle *b*.

_____

1 mark

SHAPE, SPACE AND MEASURES

Angles in parallel lines and polygons

1 Write down the values of angles *a*, *b* and *c*.

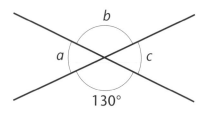

$a =$ _____ $b =$ _____ $c =$ _____

2 Write down the value of angle *d*. Give a reason for your answer.

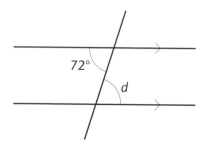

$d =$ _____ because _____

3 Write down the value of angle *e*. Give a reason for your answer.

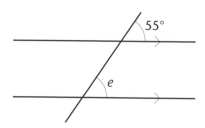

$e =$ _____ because _____

4 Write down the value of angle *f*. Give a reason for your answer.

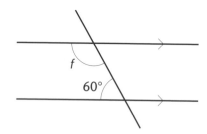

$f =$ _____ because _____

5 Write down the value of angles *g* and *h*. Give reasons for your answers.

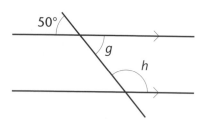

$g =$ _____ because _____

$h =$ _____ because _____

6 What is the sum of the interior angles of a pentagon?

_____

1 mark

7 Which of the following statements is true for a regular hexagon?
Tick the correct answer. (There may be more than one.)

☐ Each interior angle is 60°   ☐ Each interior angle is 120°

☐ Each exterior angle is 60°   ☐ Each exterior angle is 120°

1 mark

8 *ABCDE* is a regular pentagon.
Work out the value of angles x, y and z.

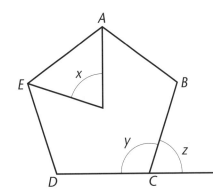

$x =$ _____ $y =$ _____ $z =$ _____

3 marks

9 The diagram shows four regular octagons,
A, B, C and D.
Explain why shape S is a square.

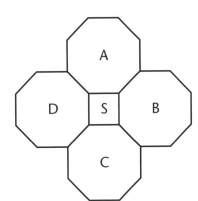

_____

_____

_____

2 marks

Reflections and rotations

1 The grid shows a shaded triangle that has been rotated **clockwise** to the triangle A.

   a What is the angle of rotation?

   _____

   b Mark the centre of rotation on the grid.

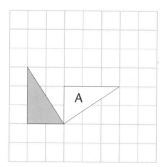

1 mark

1 mark

2 The grid shows triangle A that has been reflected onto triangle B.

   Draw the mirror line on the grid.

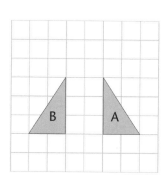

1 mark

3 The grid shows two transformations of the shaded triangle.

   a Describe fully the **single** transformation that takes the shaded triangle to triangle A.

   _____

   _____

   b Describe fully the **single** transformation that takes the shaded triangle to triangle B.

   _____

   _____

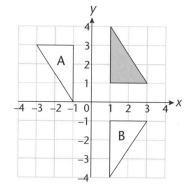

3 marks

2 marks

4 Draw the reflection of the shape shown in the mirror line $x = -1$.

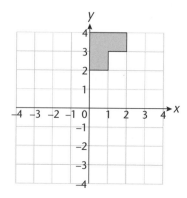

1 mark

5 Reflect the given shape in the line $y = x$.

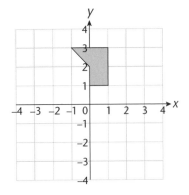

1 mark

6 Rotate the shaded triangle anticlockwise by 90° about (–1, 0).

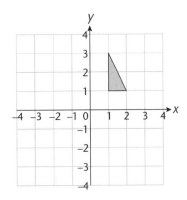

1 mark

7 Describe fully the transformation that takes the shaded triangle to

a triangle A

_____

_____

b triangle B

_____

_____

c triangle C

_____

_____

_____

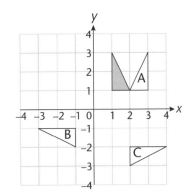

2 marks

2 marks

3 marks

SHAPE, SPACE AND MEASURES

Enlargements

1 Shapes A and B are enlargements of the shaded shape.

What is the scale factor of each enlargement?

A _____

B _____

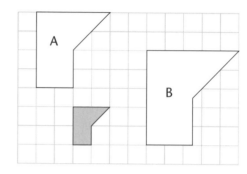

2 marks

2 The white shape is an enlargement of the shaded shape with scale factor 2.

One 'ray' joining points is shown.

Draw the other rays to find the centre of enlargement.

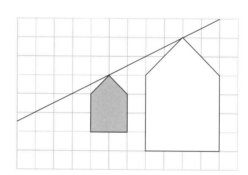

1 mark

3 On the grid, draw an enlargement of the triangle with a scale factor of 2.

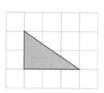

1 mark

4 On the grid, draw an enlargement of the shape with a scale factor of 3.

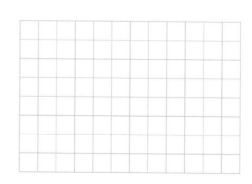

1 mark

5 The triangle *ABC* is enlarged to a triangle *A'B'C'* by a scale factor of 2 about the origin.

Write down the coordinates of the points *A'*, *B'* and *C'*.

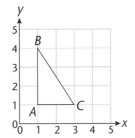

A' (_____ , _____)

B' (_____ , _____)

C' (_____ , _____)

3 marks

6 The triangle *A'B'C'* has been enlarged from a triangle *ABC* by a scale factor of 3 about the origin.

Write down the coordinates of the points *A*, *B* and *C*.

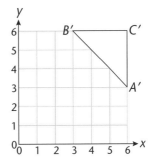

A (_____ , _____)

B (_____ , _____)

C (_____ , _____)

3 marks

7 The shaded triangle has been transformed to triangles A, B and C.

Match the triangle to the transformation described below.

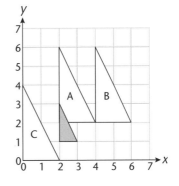

a Enlargement scale factor 2 about (0, 0) is

_____

b Enlargement scale factor 2 about (2, 0) is

_____

c Enlargement scale factor 2 about (4, 2) is

_____

3 marks

SHAPE, SPACE AND MEASURES

3-D shapes

1 Look at the net.
What is the name of the shape that will
be formed by this net?

_____

1 mark

2 Which of the following are nets for a cube?

a   **b**   **c**   **d**

_____

1 mark

3 This is the plan and elevation for a solid.

What is the name of this solid?

_____

PLAN   **ELEVATION**

1 mark

4 For this solid, draw
   a the plan
   b the elevation from X
   c the elevation from Y

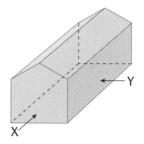

3 marks

5 How many planes of symmetry do the following shapes have?

a    **b**   **c**

3 marks

_____   _____   _____

6 The shape shown is made from six centimetre cubes.

Draw **a** the plan
b the elevation from A

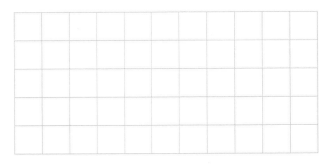

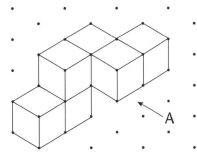

2 marks

7 A shape is made from four centimetre cubes.
The plan and two side elevations are shown below.

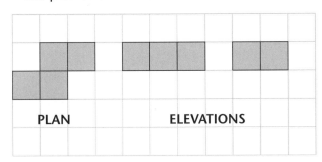

PLAN   ELEVATIONS

Draw an isometric view of the shape.

2 marks

8 A cylinder has a height of h and a radius of r.

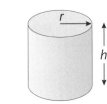

a Which of the following is the formula for the
surface area of the cylinder?

i $\pi r^2 + rh$ **ii** $2\pi r^2 + 2\pi rh$ **iii** $\pi r^2 h$

_____ **1 mark**

b Work out **i** the volume and **ii** the surface area of
a cylinder with height 10 cm and radius 6 cm.
Give your answers to 3 significant figures.

i Volume cm³ **2 marks**

ii Surface area cm² **2 marks**

9 Work out the surface area of a cuboid with
length 12 cm, width 6 cm and height 8 cm.

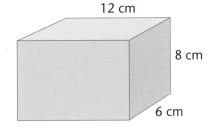

_____ cm² **2 marks**

SHAPE, SPACE AND MEASURES

Perimeter and area

1 What is **a** the perimeter and **b** the area of this right-angled triangle?

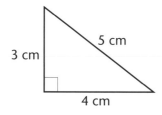

    a perimeter _____

    b area _____

2 Work out **a** the perimeter and **b** the area of this isosceles triangle.

Remember to include the units in your answer.

    a perimeter _____

    b area _____

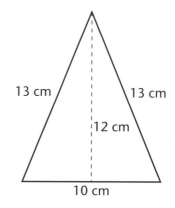

3 A, B, C and D are triangles drawn on a centimetre grid.
What are the areas of triangles A, B, C and D?

A _____ cm²

B _____ cm²

C _____ cm²

D _____ cm²

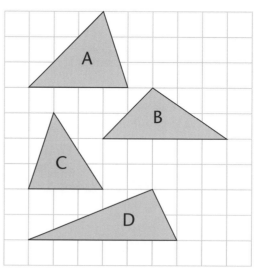

4 What is the area of this parallelogram?

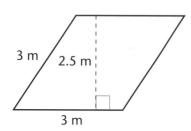

_____

5 What is the area of this trapezium?

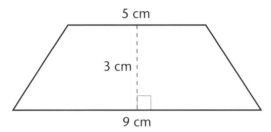

5 cm

3 cm

9 cm

_____ **2 marks**

6 All of the following shapes have the same area.

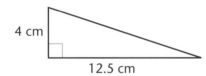

4 cm

12.5 cm

x

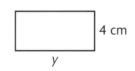

4 cm

y

a Find the value of x.

_____ **1 mark**

b Find the value of y.

_____ **1 mark**

7 Find the area of this shape.

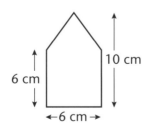

6 cm

10 cm

←6 cm→

_____ **2 marks**

SHAPE, SPACE AND MEASURES

Circumference and area of a circle

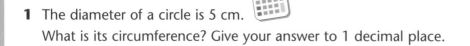

level
6

1 The diameter of a circle is 5 cm.
What is its circumference? Give your answer to 1 decimal place.

_____ cm   **1 mark**

2 The radius of a circle is 4 m.
What is its circumference? Give your answer to 1 decimal place.

_____ m   **1 mark**

3 The circumference of a circle is 25 cm.
What is its diameter? Give your answer to the nearest centimetre.

_____ cm   **1 mark**

4 A tin of beans has a diameter of 7.5 cm.
The label around the tin has an overlap of 1 cm.
What is the length of the label?
Give your answer to 1 decimal place.
Remember to include the units in your answer.

_____   **2 marks**

5 What is the perimeter of this semicircle?
Give your answer to 1 decimal place.

_____ cm

10 cm   **1 mark**

6 The radius of a circle is 3 cm.
What is its area? Give your answer to 1 decimal place.

_____ cm^2 **1 mark**

7 The diameter of a circle is 5 cm.
What is its area?
Remember to include the units in your answer.

_____ **2 marks**

8 A circle has a diameter of 18 cm.
What is its area?
Give your answer as a multiple of π.

_____ cm² **1 mark**

9 What is the area of this quadrant?
Give your answer to 1 decimal place.

_____ cm²

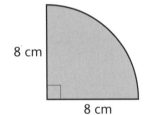

8 cm

8 cm

1 mark

10 What is the area of the shaded part
of the diagram?
Give your answer to 1 decimal place.

_____ cm²

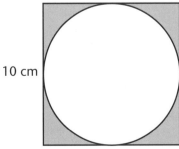

10 cm

10 cm

1 mark

SHAPE, SPACE AND MEASURES

Volume

1 **a** What is the volume of this cuboid?

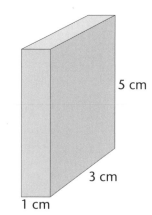

_____ cm³

5 cm

1 mark

b What is the surface area?

_____ cm²

3 cm

1 cm

1 mark

2 A cuboid has a volume of 36 cm³.
Its length is 6 cm and its width is 3 cm.
What is the height of the cuboid?

_____ cm **1 mark**

3 A cuboid has a volume of 200 cm³.
Its length and width are 5 cm.
What is the surface area?
Remember to include the units in your answer.

_____ **2 marks**

4 The volume of a cube is 64 cm³.
What is the length of each edge of the cube?

_____ cm **1 mark**

5 The surface area of this cuboid is 184 cm².
Work out the length of the cuboid.

4 cm

5 cm

_____ cm

1 mark

6 This is a net of a cuboid.
What is the volume of the cuboid?

2 m

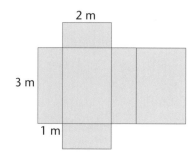

3 m

_____ m³

1 m

1 mark

7 Here are four cuboids.

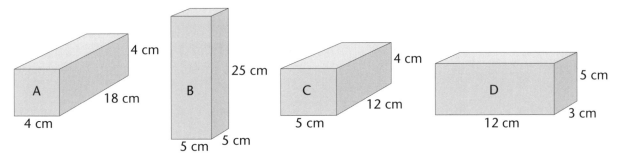

Rearrange the cuboids in the order
of their volume, with the smallest first.

_____ **1 mark**

8 A tank has the following measurements.
How many litres of water can it hold?

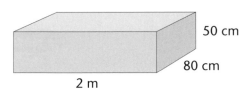

_____ litres **2 marks**

9 These two cuboids have the same volume. What is the value of *x*?

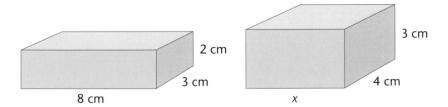

_____ cm **1 mark**

SHAPE, SPACE AND MEASURES

Constructions

1 Construct an angle of 60° at the point *A* on the line *AB*.

A •————————————• B

2 marks

2 Construct the perpendicular bisector of the line *AB*.

A •————————————• B

2 marks

3 Construct the angle bisector of the angle *ABC*.

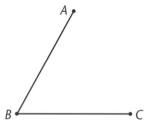

2 marks

4 Draw this triangle accurately.

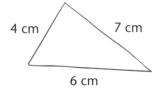

2 marks

5 Draw this triangle accurately.

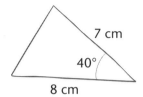

6 Draw this triangle accurately.

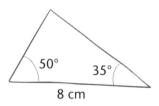

SHAPE, SPACE AND MEASURES

Loci

1 In each of these squares shade the region described.

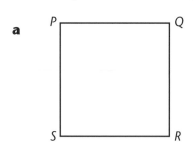

a

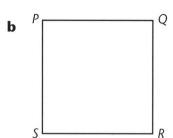

b

a All points that are nearer to *P* than to *Q*.

1 mark

b All points that are nearer to *S* than to *Q*.

1 mark

2 *ABCD* are squares of side 3 cm. Match the given loci to the diagrams.

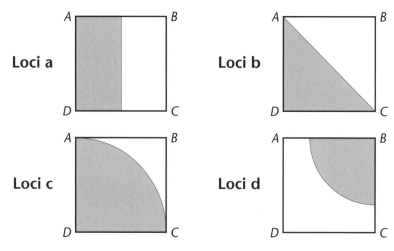

i All points nearer to *D* than to *B*. _____

ii All points within 3 cm of *D*. _____

iii All points nearer to the line *AD* than the line *BC*. _____

iv All points within 2 cm of *B*. _____

4 marks

3 Construct the locus of the point that is the same distance from the lines *AB* and *AC*.

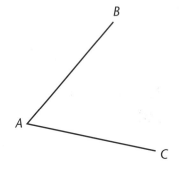

2 marks

4 The diagram shows an island with two airports A and B.
The scale is 1 cm represents 10 km.
A radar station at A picks up aircraft within 30 km.
A radar station at B picks up aircraft within 40 km.

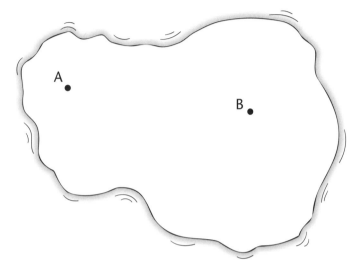

a Does the radar station at B pick up an aircraft flying directly over A? _____

b Show all the points where aircraft are picked up by both radar stations.

2 marks

5 The diagram shows a garden with a garden shed.
Each grid square represents 50 cm.

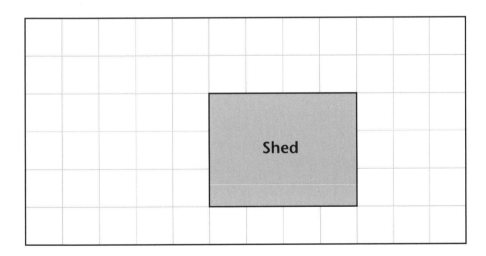

A tree is to be planted. It must not be planted within 1 m of
the edge of the garden or the shed.
Shade clearly the area in which the tree can be planted.

1 mark

SHAPE, SPACE AND MEASURES

Similarity

1 Look at the five triangles below. All lengths are centimetres.

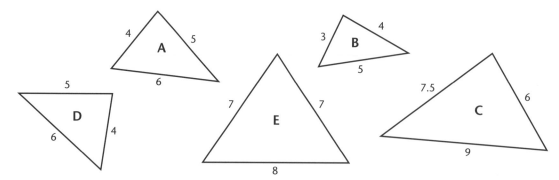

a Which two triangles are congruent to each other? Explain why.

_____

1 mark

b Which two triangles are similar to each other but not congruent? Explain why.

_____

1 mark

2 These two triangles are similar.

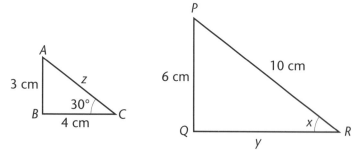

a What is the scale factor between
triangle *ABC* and triangle *PQR?* _____

1 mark

b Write down the value of angle *x*. _____ °

1 mark

c Write down the length of the side *y*. _____ cm

1 mark

d Write down the length of the side *z*. _____ cm

1 mark

3 Look at the two similar quadrilaterals, *ABCD* and *PQRS*.

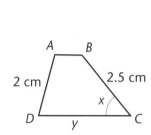
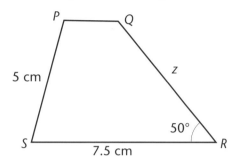

a What is the scale factor between
   quadrilaterals *ABCD* and *PQRS*? _____

b Write down the value of angle *x*. _____ °

c Write down the length of the side *y*. _____ cm

d Write down the length of the side *z*. _____ cm

4 Lines *AB* and *PQ* are parallel.

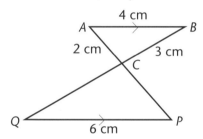

a Explain why triangles *ABC* and *CPQ* are similar. _____

   _____

b Write down the value of the length *CP*. _____ cm

c Write down the value of the length *CQ*. _____ cm

5 Below are three tins of different sizes.

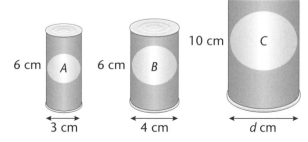

a Explain why tin *A* is not similar to tin *B*. _____

b Tin *C* is similar to tin *B*. Find the diameter, *d*, of tin *C*. _____ cm

Pythagoras' theorem

1 A square of side length 5 cm has been drawn inside a circle.

a What is the area of the square?

_____ cm²

1 mark

b Work out the diameter of the circle.

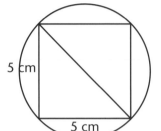

5 cm

5 cm

_____ cm

1 mark

c Work out the area of the circle.

Give your answer to 3 significant figures. _____ cm²

1 mark

2 In triangle ABC side $AB = 7$ cm, side $BC = 10$ cm.

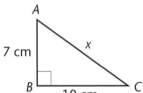

A

7 cm

x

B 10 cm *C*

Calculate the length of the side AC.

Give your answer to 3 significant figures. _____ cm

2 marks

3 In triangle ABC side $AB = 6$ cm, side $AC = 12$ cm.

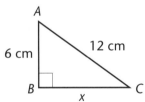

A

6 cm

12 cm

B *x* *C*

Calculate the length of the side BC.

Give your answer to 3 significant figures. _____ cm

2 marks

4 A plane flies 30 km east and 20 km north.
It then flies directly back to its starting point.

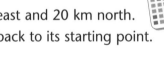

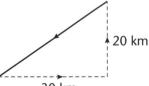

20 km

30 km

Calculate the total distance travelled. _____ km

2 marks

5 Alton and Brompton are two towns.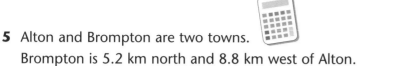
Brompton is 5.2 km north and 8.8 km west of Alton.

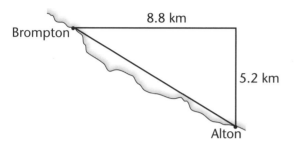

Calculate the direct distance from Alton to Brompton.

_____ km

6 Triangle *ABC* has sides of 1.8 cm, 8 cm and 8.2 cm.

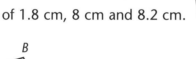

Is triangle *ABC* right-angled?
Justify your answer. _____

7 A circle with a diameter of 10 cm is drawn within a square.

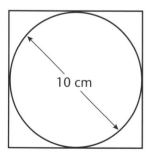

Calculate the length of the square's diagonal.
Give your answer to 3 significant figures. _____ cm

SHAPE, SPACE AND MEASURES

Trigonometry

1 Calculate the length x in this right-angled triangle.

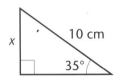

10 cm

x

35°

_____ cm   **2 marks**

2 Calculate the angle x in this right-angled triangle.

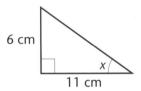

6 cm

x

11 cm

_____ degrees   **2 marks**

3 Calculate the length x in this right-angled triangle.

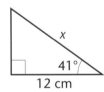

x

41°

12 cm

_____ cm   **2 marks**

4 In triangle *ACB* side *AB* = 6 cm, side *AC* = 12 cm.

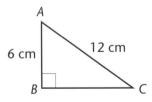

A

12 cm

6 cm

B   *C*

Calculate the size of the angle *ACB*.   _____ degrees   **2 marks**

5 A plane flies 30 km east and 20 km north.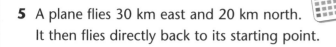
It then flies directly back to its starting point.

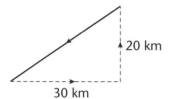

Calculate the bearing of the return flight. _____ degrees

2 marks

6 Alton and Brompton are two towns.
Brompton is 5.2 km north and 8.8 km west of Alton.

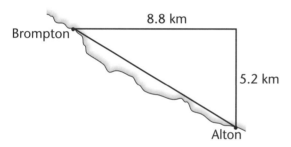

Calculate the bearing of Alton from Brompton. _____ degrees

2 marks

7 *ABC* is an isosceles triangle with sides of 6 cm, 8 cm and 8 cm.

a Calculate the height h of the triangle.

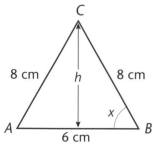

_____ cm

2 marks

b Calculate the angle marked x.

_____ degrees

2 marks

c Calculate the area of the triangle.

_____ cm²

2 marks

Sectors and circle theorems

1 A circle has the same numerical value for the circumference as the area. What is the radius?

_____ cm **2 marks**

2 A sector of a circle radius 6 cm has an angle of 72°.

   a What is the perimeter of the sector?

_____ cm **2 marks**

   b What is the area of the sector?

_____ cm² **2 marks**

3 a What fraction of 360° is **i** 90°_____ **ii** 80°_____

      2 marks

   b The diagram shows two sectors of circles A and B.

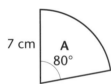 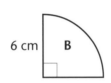

     Which sector has the bigger area? _____ **2 marks**

   c Which sector has the bigger perimeter?

_____ **2 marks**

4 Cylinder A has a diameter of 15 cm and a height of 20 cm. Cylinder B has a diameter of 20 cm and a height of 15 cm.

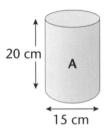 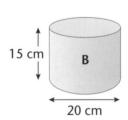

   a Which cylinder has the greater surface area?

_____ **2 marks**

   b Which cylinder has the greater volume?

_____ **2 marks**

5 Write down the value of the angles marked with letters in these diagrams.

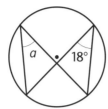 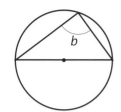

 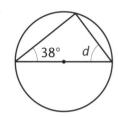

$a =$ _____ degrees

$b =$ _____ degrees

$c =$ _____ degrees

$d =$ _____ degrees

6 Write down the value of the angles marked with letters in these diagrams.

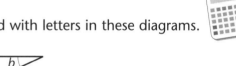

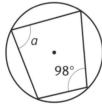

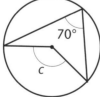

$a =$ _____ degrees

$b =$ _____ degrees

$c =$ _____ degrees

$d =$ _____ degrees

1 This grouped frequency table shows the ages of 50 members of a tennis club.
Which of the following statements could be true or must be false?

Age	Frequency
21 – 30	15
31 – 40	18
41 – 50	12
51 – 60	4
61 – 70	1
Total	50

                                                    Could be true   Must be false

a The range of the ages is 49   ☐   ☐

b The median age is 45   ☐   ☐

c The modal age is 65   ☐   ☐

d The modal age is 39   ☐   ☐

4 marks

2 The bar charts show the number of days absent in a week for students in two different classes in Year 10.

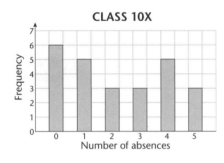

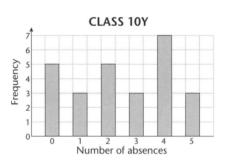

a State the modal number of absences for each class. 10X _____ 10Y _____   **2 marks**

b Work out the median number of absences for each class. 10X _____ 10Y _____   **2 marks**

c Work out the mean number of absences for each class. 10X _____ 10Y _____   **2 marks**

d Which class was worse for absentees? Give a reason for your answer.

_____

_____   **1 mark**

3 The table shows information about how late two buses are over a 20 day period.
The data is in minutes.

	Mean	Median	Mode	Range
Bus A	8	9	3	15
Bus B	8	4	0	10

Which bus is more reliable?
Give a reason for your answer.

_____

_____

2 marks

4 The following data shows the weekly wages in a small factory with eight workers.

£95   £220   £220   £220   £220   £220   £320   £700

Everyone gets a £20 a week pay rise.

Which of the following is true for the new wages?

Tick the correct answer. (There may be more than one.)

a ☐ The mean will increase by £20.

b ☐ The mode will increase by £20.

c ☐ The median will increase by £20.

d ☐ The range will increase by £20.

1 mark

5 Two girls want to be in the school senior netball team.

The number of goals they scored in their last 10 junior matches were

| Aisha | 3 | 7 | 2 | 4 | 4 | 1 | 1 | 0 | 2 | 1 |
| Betty | 3 | 4 | 2 | 3 | 3 | 1 | 2 | 2 | 3 | 2 |

a Work out the mean number of goals for each girl. _____   *2 marks*

b Work out the range for each girl.   _____   *2 marks*

c Which girl should be chosen for the senior team and why?

_____   *1 mark*

6 The data shows the number of tomatoes from 10 plants grown in a greenhouse and 10 plants grown outside.

| Greenhouse | 2 | 8 | 7 | 12 | 4 | 6 | 9 | 10 | 8 | 4 |
| Outside | 5 | 5 | 8 | 9 | 8 | 6 | 6 | 9 | 8 | 6 |

a Work out the mean number of tomatoes per plant for

i the greenhouse   _____

ii outside   _____   *2 marks*

b Work out the range for the number of tomatoes per plant for

i the greenhouse   _____

ii outside   _____   *2 marks*

c Which is the better place to grow tomatoes and why?

_____   *1 mark*

1 The graph shows the trend in the temperature
   in a garden over a week in May. The readings
   were taken at midday each day.

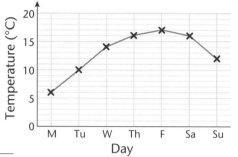

   a What was the temperature on Wednesday?

   _____

   1 mark

   b The temperature was 16 °C on 2 days.

   Which days? _____ and _____

   1 mark

   c On what day was the temperature highest? _____

   1 mark

   d Explain why you cannot tell what the
   temperature was at midnight on Wednesday. _____

   _____

   1 mark

2 The graph shows the trend in the temperature
   in a garden over a week. The temperatures
   were recorded at 12 midday and 12 midnight.

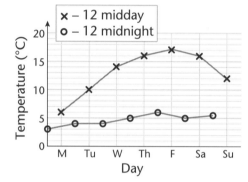

   a What was the temperature at midnight and
   midday on Monday?

   midnight _____ midday _____

   1 mark

   b What was the difference in temperatures
   between midday and midnight on Tuesday? _____

   1 mark

   c Which day had the greatest difference between
   the temperatures at midday and midnight? _____

   1 mark

3 The graph shows the miles travelled each month by a lorry driver.

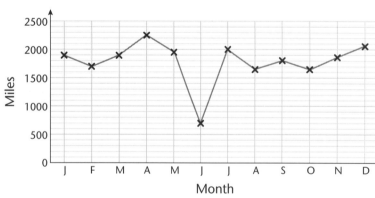

   a What was the distance he travelled in January? _____

   1 mark

   b What was the total distance travelled in the first three months of the year?

   _____

   1 mark

   c Which month was he most likely to be on holiday? _____

   1 mark

4 The graph shows the results of an experiment to see if a detergent has any effect on bacteria. Results were recorded every hour from 10 am to 4 pm.

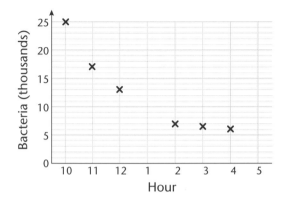

a The scientist was at lunch at 1 pm.

Estimate the number of bacteria at 1 pm.

Give your answer to the nearest 100. _____

1 mark

b When the number of bacteria drop below 5000 the detergent is said to be effective.

The scientist claimed that this graph shows that this detergent is effective.

Is this claim true or false? Give a reason for your answer.

_____

1 mark

c Is it possible to estimate the number of bacteria at 11.30 am?

Give a reason for your answer.

_____

1 mark

5 The graph shows the depth of water in a drain during a heavy rainstorm.

When the depth gets to 30 cm the area will flood.

John predicts that the area will flood by 2 pm.

Is this claim justified? Explain your answer.

_____

_____

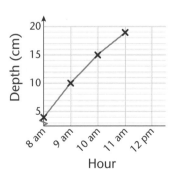

1 mark

1 Look at the frequency diagram which compares the heights of men and women in a church choir. Comment on the differences in the distributions between the men and the women.

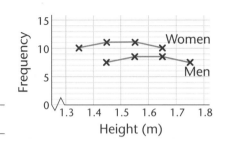

_____

_____

2 marks

2 The data shows the number of e-mails received over 15 days.

7, 12, 22, 17, 11, 9, 8, 13, 15, 21, 19, 18, 8, 8, 13

Show the data in a stem-and-leaf diagram using the key 1 | 2 represents 12.

1 mark

3 The stem-and-leaf diagram shows the ages of 12 members of a chess club.

1	3	8	9
2	0 2	2 2	3 5 8
3	1	4	

Key: 1 | 3 represents 13 years.

a How old is the oldest member? _____

1 mark

b What is the modal age of the members? _____

1 mark

c What is the range of the ages of the members? _____

1 mark

4 The table shows information on colours of cars in a car park.

Colour	Frequency	Angle
Blue	9	
White	4	
Silver	7	
Total	20	

a Complete the column for the angle that each colour would have on a pie chart.

2 marks

b Draw a pie chart to show the information.

2 marks

5 Look at the pie chart which shows the favourite drinks of some people.
48 students chose coffee.
How many students altogether were in the survey?

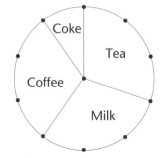

_____

1 mark

6 The pie chart shows the results of an election survey.

It is not drawn accurately.

120 people said they would vote Labour.

How many people said they would vote Green?

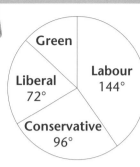

_____

1 mark

7 Which of the following could not be the angles of the sectors in a pie chart?

Tick the correct answer.

a ☐ 90°, 60°, 130°, 80°   **b** ☐ 75°, 25°, 200°, 60°

c ☐ 62°, 144°, 96°, 48°   **d** ☐ 90°, 90°, 90°, 90°

1 mark

8 Phyllis did a survey about the month people were born in.

She surveyed 240 people.

Which of the following would be a valid reason why a pie chart is not a good method of representing the data?

Tick the correct answer.

a ☐ There are too many sectors to show a valid comparison.

b ☐ 240 doesn't divide into 360 exactly.

c ☐ People might lie about their birthday.

d ☐ You couldn't fit the labels on the pie chart.

1 mark

9 The table shows information about the nationality of people on a plane.

	British	American	French	German
Percentage	45%	25%	20%	10%

Draw a pie chart to represent the data.

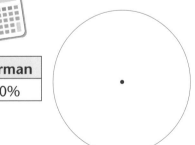

1 mark

10 Draw a pie chart to represent this data.

Blue	Silver	Black
12	6	2

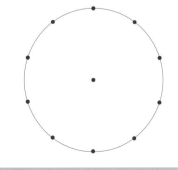

1 mark

1 Correlation can be described using the following terms.

S Strong positive correlation   **W** Weak positive correlation

N No correlation

G Strong negative correlation   **K** Weak negative correlation

a Match each diagram with one of the descriptions above.

i  _____   **ii**  _____   **iii**  _____   **iv** 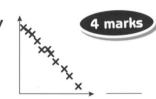 _____

4 marks

b Match the types of correlation to these comparisons.

i The age of a car and its top speed. _____

ii The number of men building a wall and the time taken to build it. _____

iii The number of ice creams sold and the temperature. _____

iv The value of cars and their age. _____

4 marks

2 The scatter graph shows the heights and weights of a breed of horses.

a Draw a line of best fit on the data.

1 mark

b A horse of the same breed has a weight of 232 kg. Estimate its height.

_____

1 mark

c Another horse has a weight of 200 kg and is 200 cm tall.

Could this horse be of the same breed?

Give a reason for your answer.

_____

1 mark

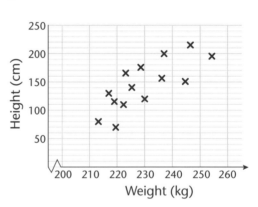

3 The graph shows the finishing times of runners in a marathon and the number of miles run per week in training. A line of best fit has been drawn.

Neil runs 120 miles a week in training.

What is his likely finishing time?

_____

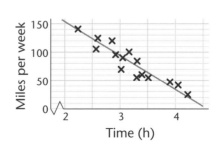

1 mark

4 The scatter graph shows the ages and number of years in the job for the men and women employed in a do-it-yourself store.

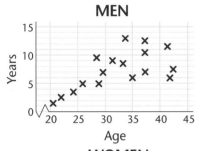

MEN

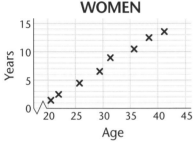

WOMEN

Which of the following statements is true for the data?
Tick the correct answer. (There may be more than one.)

a ☐ The women's scatter graph shows strong positive correlation.

b ☐ The men's scatter graph shows strong positive correlation.

c ☐ There are more men employed than women.

d ☐ For men over 30 there is no correlation between their age and the number of years employed.

1 mark

5 Three different variables are:

A the time it takes to plaster a wall

B the number of men working on a job

C the weekly wage bill

Which of the following will be true?
Tick the correct answer. (There may be more than one.)

a ☐ A and B will show negative correlation.

b ☐ A and C will show no correlation.

c ☐ B and C will show negative correlation.

d ☐ B and C will show positive correlation.

1 mark

6 The scatter graph shows the ages and finishing times in a marathon for 10 members of a running club.

a Describe the correlation.

_____

1 mark

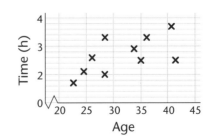

b Draw a line of best fit on the data.

1 mark

c Another member of the club is 45 years old. What is his likely finishing time?

_____

1 mark

1 When carrying out a survey which of the following should you do?
Tick the correct answer. (There may be more than one.)

a ☐ Ask friends, relatives or neighbours.

b ☐ Ask a variety of people.

c ☐ Ask questions that are unbiased.

d ☐ Make sure there is an equal number of boys and girls.

1 mark

2 Jodie does a survey to find out people's views on the following question.
'Should school uniform be worn by all students?'

a Say why each of the following would not be good responses to this question.

i Yes ☐ No ☐ Criticism _____

_____

1 mark

ii Agree ☐ Don't know ☐ Disagree ☐

Criticism _____

1 mark

iii Ties ☐ Blazers ☐ Shoes ☐ Caps ☐

Criticism _____

1 mark

b Say why this is a good response to the same question.

| Strongly agree ☐ | Agree somewhat ☐ | Neither agree nor disagree ☐ | Disagree somewhat ☐ | Strongly Disagree ☐ |

Reason _____

1 mark

3 Give two reasons why this is not a good survey question.
'People who smoke are not very intelligent. Don't you agree?'

Reason 1 _____

1 mark

Reason 2 _____

1 mark

4 Four students are doing a survey on sport.
Asif decides to ask 30 students in the Badminton club.
Benny decides to ask his Year 9 tutor group.
Colin decides to ask 30 students on the school field at lunchtime.
Derek gets a list of all the students in school sand randomly selects 30 names to ask.
Who will get the most reliable results? Give a reason for your answer.

Reason _____

1 mark

5 What is wrong with this question on eye colour?

What is your eye colour?	**Brown** Yes/No	**Blue** Yes/No

Reason _____

1 mark

6 The headmaster gets an alphabetical list of all the students in the school and sends a questionnaire to every tenth name on the list.
Explain why this will give a good sample of the students.

Reason _____

1 mark

7 In a clothing factory there are 100 women employees and 15 men employees.
The managing director sends a questionnaire to the men and 15 of the women.
Explain why this will not give a representative sample.

Reason _____

1 mark

8 Jade does a survey to find out people's views on the following question.
'Did you learn anything from the lesson?'

   a Say why each of the following would not be good responses to this question.

      i

Yes ☐	No ☐

      Criticism _____

      _____

1 mark

      ii

A bit ☐	Don't know ☐	A lot ☐

      Criticism _____

      _____

1 mark

      iii

Pythagoras ☐	Trigonometry ☐

      Criticism _____

      _____

1 mark

   b Say why this is a good response to the same question.

Mark on a scale from 1 (learnt a lot) to 5 (learnt little)
1   2   3   4   5

Reason _____

_____

_____

1 mark

9 There are 2000 students in a school.
To find out their views on vegetarianism some students do a survey. Melinda surveys 10 students picked at random from the school roll. Nandi surveys 30 students picked at random from the school roll. Owen surveys 100 students picked at random from the school roll.
Who will get the most reliable results? Give a reason for your answer.

Reason _____

_____

1 mark

Box plots and cumulative frequency diagrams

1 The box plot shows the weights of marrows grown in a greenhouse.

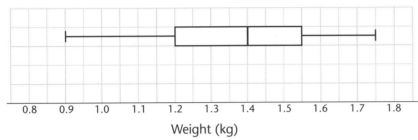

0.8   0.9   1.0   1.1   1.2   1.3   1.4   1.5   1.6   1.7   1.8

Weight (kg)

Below is some data about the weight of marrows grown outside.

Lowest value	Lower quartile	Median	Upper quartile	Highest value
0.8 kg	1.0 kg	1.3 kg	1.45 kg	1.6 kg

  a On the same diagram draw the box plot for the weights of the marrows grown outside.

2 marks

  b Comment on the difference between the average weight of the marrows grown outside and those grown inside.

_____

1 mark

  c Comment on the difference between the consistency of the weight of the marrows grown outside and those grown inside.

_____

1 mark

2 The box plot shows the marks (out of 10) for the boys in form 7B in a mathematics quiz.

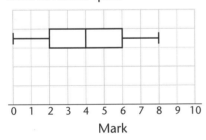

0   1   2   3   4   5   6   7   8   9   10

Mark

  a The distribution of marks for the boys is symmetrical.

Explain how you can tell.

_____

1 mark

  b The following is information about the marks for the girls in 7B on the same quiz.

- The median mark was the same as the upper quartile for the boys.
- The lowest mark for the girls was the same as the lowest mark for the boys.
- The range of the girls' marks was 1 more than the range of the boys.
- The upper quartile for the girls was 1 more than their median.
- The interquartile range for the girls was the same as the interquartile range for the boys.

Use this information to draw a box plot for the girls on the same diagram.

2 marks

3 The cumulative frequency graph shows the heights of 100 girls.

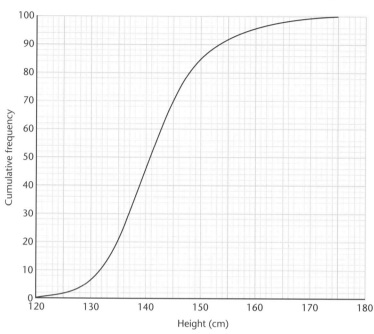

a Use the graph to estimate

i the median height

_____ cm

ii the interquartile range

_____ cm

b How many girls are over 155 cm?

_____

1 mark

4 The cumulative frequency graph shows the diameters of 60 oak trees in a wood.
The box plot shows the diameters of 60 oak trees in a parkland.

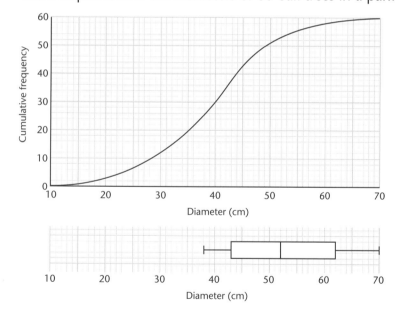

a What is the interquartile range and median of the oak trees in the wood?

interquartile range _____ median _____

b What is the interquartile range and median of the oak trees in the parkland?

interquartile range _____ median _____

c Comment on the differences between the distributions of the diameters of the trees in the wood and the parkland.

_____

_____

2 marks

HANDLING DATA Probability 1

1 In a youth club, the probability that a member picked at random is a girl is $\frac{4}{7}$.
What is the probability that a member picked at random is a boy?

_____

1 mark

2 A bag contains 1 blue and 4 red balls.
Some blue balls are to be added to the bag to make the chance of picking a blue ball at random $\frac{1}{2}$.
How many blue balls should be added? _____

1 mark

3 A box of toffees contains nut and plain. The probability of getting a plain toffee is $\frac{9}{20}$. What is the probability of getting a nut toffee?

_____

1 mark

4 Here are four events.

A Throwing a three with a dice.

B Picking a vowel at random from the letters:

D I S T R I B U T I O N

C The next person that comes into the room has a birthday in January.

D Throwing a number that is a factor of 24 with an ordinary dice.

Mark each event on the following probability scale.

0                       $\frac{1}{2}$ 1

2 marks

5 This bag contains 4 white balls, 6 black balls and 5 striped balls.
A ball is taken from the bag at random.

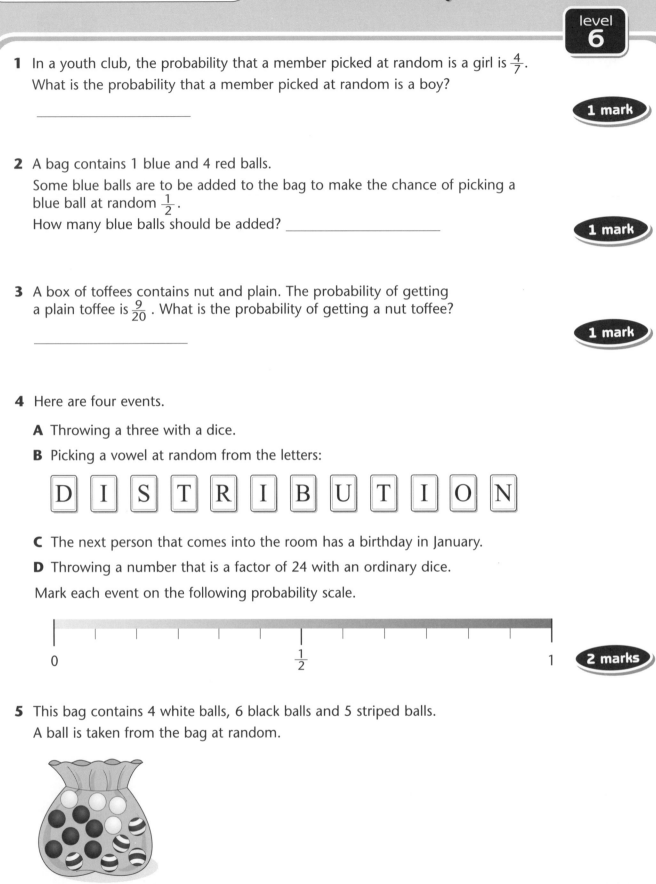

a What is the probability it is black? _____

1 mark

b What is the probability it is not striped? _____

1 mark

6 The following cards are placed face down and shuffled.

 S T A T I S T I C S

a A card is picked at random. What is the probability it is **not** a letter S or a letter T?

_____

1 mark

b A card is picked at random. It is a vowel. **It is thrown away**.
Another card is picked at random.
What is the probability it is a letter **S or T**?

_____

1 mark

7 A bag contains 10 coloured balls.
A ball is taken out, its colour noted and then replaced.
This is repeated 1000 times.
The results are red 822 times, blue 178 times.
How many **a** red balls   **b** blue balls are in the bag?

Red _____   Blue _____

2 marks

8 The sample space diagram shows the outcomes from throwing two coins.
There are four outcomes altogether.

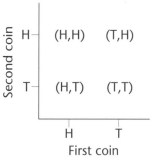

a What is the probability of throwing two heads with two coins?

_____

1 mark

b What is the probability of throwing a head and a tail in any order with two coins?

_____

1 mark

9 The sample space diagram shows the outcomes for throwing two dice.

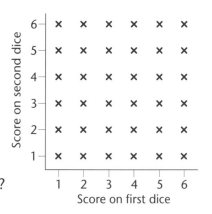

a What is the probability of throwing a 'double', i.e. the same score on each dice?

_____

1 mark

b What is the probability of a score of 4?

_____

1 mark

c What is the probability of a score of 10 or over?

_____

1 mark

1 A bag contains 1 blue and 4 red balls.

A ball is taken from the bag and **not replaced**.

Another ball is then taken out at random.

   a If the first ball taken out is blue, what is the probability that the second ball taken out is

      i blue? _____ `1 mark`

      ii red? _____ `1 mark`

   b If the first ball taken out is red, what is the probability that the second ball taken out is

      i blue? _____ `1 mark`

      ii red? _____ `1 mark`

2 This bag contains 4 white balls and 6 black balls.

A ball is taken from the bag at random and then replaced.

Another ball is then taken from the bag.

   a Complete the tree diagram.

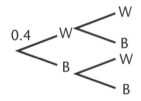

`1 mark`

   b What is the probability that the balls are

      i both white? _____ `2 marks`

      ii both black? _____ `2 marks`

3 This bag contains 4 white balls and 6 black balls.

A ball is taken from the bag at random and **not** replaced.

Another ball is then taken out.

   a What is the probability that both balls are black?

      _____ `2 marks`

   b What is the probability that both balls are the same colour?

      _____ `2 marks`

4 Two bags contain red and blue balls. Bag A has 5 red and 4 blue balls.

Bag B has 4 red and 3 blue balls. I can choose a ball from either bag.

I want to choose a red ball. Which bag should I choose?

      _____ `2 marks`

5 A company makes pens. The company knows that the probability that any pen will be defective is $\frac{1}{25}$.

   a A box contains 1000 pens. How many of the pens are likely to be defective?

   _____   **1 mark**

   b Two pens are tested at random. Calculate the probability that both pens are defective.

   _____   **2 marks**

   c Calculate the probability that only one of the two pens will be defective.

   _____   **2 marks**

6 **a** A fair dice is thrown once. What is the probability of scoring

   i 2? _____

   ii any value other than 2? _____   **2 marks**

   b A game costs 10p a go. A fair dice is thrown twice.

   If it lands on a 2 twice then the player wins £1. If it lands on 2 once in the two throws the player gets their 10p back. If it does not land on 2 in either throw the player loses their money.

   i Show that the probability of getting your money back is $\frac{10}{36}$.

   _____   **2 marks**

   ii Simon has 36 goes. How much can he expect to win or lose?

   _____   **2 marks**

7 A bag contains 20 balls. The balls are either white or black. Four people take balls out and replace them a different number of times.

Person	Pete	Rose	Sue	Tom
Number of goes	10	50	100	1000
White balls	3	18	33	320
Black balls	7	32	67	680

   a Which person's results are the most reliable? Give a reason why.

   _____   **1 mark**

   b Estimate how many balls of each colour there are in the bag. Justify your answer.

   _____

   _____   **2 marks**

Practice Paper 1

Time allowed 60 minutes.
You may **<u>not</u>** use a calculator on this paper.

1 This quadrilateral has one acute angle and three obtuse angles.

a Now draw a quadrilateral which has two acute angles and two obtuse angles.

1 mark

b Explain why you cannot draw a quadrilateral which has four acute angles.

_____

1 mark

2 Anna buys a box of chocolates that are all the same size and shape. The box contains 12 milk chocolates, 8 plain chocolates and 5 white chocolates.
Anna takes a chocolate from the box at random.

a What is the probability that she takes a milk chocolate? _____

1 mark

b What is the probability that she takes a plain chocolate? _____

1 mark

c What is the probability that she does not take a white chocolate? _____

1 mark

3 A single ticket on the metro costs £1.35.
Dave buys a book of 25 single tickets, which costs him £30.
How much does Dave save by buying a book of tickets?

£ _____

2 marks

4 When $a = 6$, $b = 5$ and $c = 2$,

a work out the value of the following:

$a + 2b + c$

_____

1 mark

$3a + b - 2c$

_____

1 mark

b If $a + b + c + d = 20$, work out the value of d.

_____

1 mark

5 a Complete the following sentences.

_____ out of 200 is the same as 40%

1 mark

30 out of 50 is the same as _____ %

1 mark

b _____ out of _____ is the same as 5%

1 mark

6 Here is a fraction strip.

$\frac{1}{2}$		

$\frac{1}{3}$		

$\frac{1}{4}$			

| $\frac{1}{12}$ | | | | | | | | | | | |

Use the fraction strip to help you work out the following:

$\frac{1}{2} + \frac{5}{12} =$

_____

1 mark

$\frac{1}{4} + \frac{1}{3} =$

_____

1 mark

$\frac{3}{4} - \frac{5}{12} =$

_____

1 mark

7 **a** Complete the table for the mapping $y = x + 5$.

x	2	4	6
y	7		

1 mark

b Complete the table for the mapping $y = 2x - 3$.

x	2	4	6
y	1		

1 mark

c Write down the mapping for this table.

x	2	4	6
y	2	3	4

 $y =$ _____

1 mark

8 Here are three cuboids.

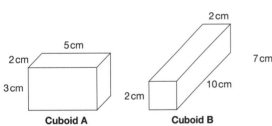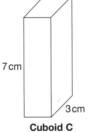

Cuboid A   Cuboid B   Cuboid C

a Which of the cuboids has the largest surface area?
Tick (✓) the correct box.

Cuboid A ☐   Cuboid B ☐   Cuboid C ☐

2 marks

b Which of the cuboids has the largest volume?
Tick (✓) the correct box.

Cuboid A ☐   Cuboid B ☐   Cuboid C ☐

2 marks

c Cuboid D has the same volume as Cuboid A.
Cuboid D has a length of 10 cm and width of 3 cm.
What is its height?

 _____ cm

1 mark

9 Three quadrilaterals are drawn on square grids below.

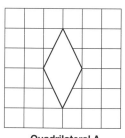 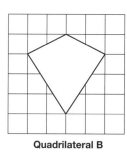 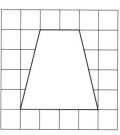

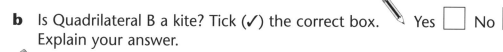

Quadrilateral A   Quadrilateral B   Quadrilateral C

a Is Quadrilateral A a square? Tick (✓) the correct box. Yes ☐ No ☐
Explain your answer.

_____

1 mark

b Is Quadrilateral B a kite? Tick (✓) the correct box. Yes ☐ No ☐
Explain your answer.

_____

1 mark

c Is Quadrilateral C a parallelogram? Tick (✓) the correct box. Yes ☐ No ☐
Explain your answer.

_____

1 mark

10 Fill in the missing numbers in the boxes.

12 + ☐ = 10

1 mark

6 – ☐ = 10

1 mark

–2 × ☐ = 10

1 mark

11 Work out $\frac{2}{3} \times \frac{3}{8}$

Write your answer as a fraction in its simplest form. _____

2 marks

12

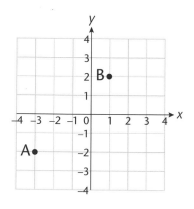

a What are the coordinates of the point A?

(_____ , _____)

1 mark

b What are the coordinates of the mid-point of AB?

(_____ , _____)

1 mark

13 Solve the following equations.

$2x + 3 = 11$ $x =$ _____

1 mark

$3(y - 2) = 9$ $y =$ _____

1 mark

$3z - 4 = z + 2$ $z =$ _____

1 mark

14 Rearrange the following equations.

$x + y = 7$ $x =$ _____

1 mark

$3w = z$ $w =$ _____

1 mark

15 Multiply out the expression $(x + 3)(x - 4)$.
Write your answer as simply as possible.

_____

2 marks

16 The scatter graph shows the arm span and height for 10 students.

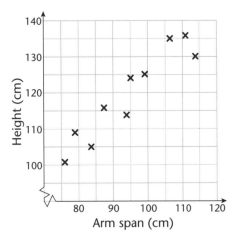

  a Describe the relationship between arm span and height.

_____

1 mark

  b Draw a line of best fit on the scatter graph.

1 mark

  c A student grows 10 cm in height in a year.
By how much would you expect the arm
span to increase? _____ cm

1 mark

  d A baby has a height at birth of 35 cm. Can you use the scatter graph to
predict the baby's arm span?
Explain your answer.

_____

1 mark

17 15 members of a slimming club record their weights before and after dieting for 3 months. The stem-and-leaf diagrams show the weights before and after the diet.

Before								After						
5								5	4	4	6	9		
6	5	7	9					6	3	5	6	8	4	
7	2	3	6	6	6	9		7	1	2	2	2	9	
8	0	2	4	8				8	3					
9	2	5						9						

Key:

7 | 2 means 72 kg

Complete the following sentences.

a Before the diet the heaviest person was —————kg and ——————— members of the club were over 70 kg.

1 mark

b After the diet the heaviest person was ———————kg and ——————— members of the club were over 70 kg.

1 mark

c Before the diet the modal weight was ———————kg and the range of the weights was ——————— kg.

1 mark

18 a Work out 27 x 33.

2 marks

b A 2 digit number is multiplied by another 2 digit number. What is the least number of digits the answer could have? Explain your answer.

1 mark

What is the greatest number of digits the answer could have? Explain your answer.

1 mark

19 A box contains some black and white counters.
There are 10 counters in the box altogether.
Amy and Zara do an experiment to find out how many counters of each colour there are in the box.
They each take a counter at random, record the colour and replace the counter.
The table shows their results.

Pupil	Number of trials	Number of black counters	Number of white counters
Amy	100	36	64
Zara	500	210	290

   a Using Amy's results, obtain an estimate of the probability of taking a black counter from the box.

1 mark

   b Using Zara's results, obtain an estimate of the probability of taking a white counter from the box.

1 mark

   c Which of the two probabilities in **a** and **b** is likely to be the more accurate? Give a reason for your answer.

1 mark

20 Work out the following.
Give your answers in standard form.

$1.2 \times 10^4 \times 2 \times 10^2 =$

1 mark

$1.2 \times 10^8 \div 2 \times 10^2 =$

1 mark

21 a and b are connected by the relationship $a^b = 64$.
One possible pair of values is $a = 8$, $b = 2$.
Give 3 other possible pairs of values for a and b that satisfy the relationship.

$a =$ _____ $b =$ _____

$a =$ _____ $b =$ _____

$a =$ _____ $b =$ _____

3 marks

Practice Paper 2

Time allowed 60 minutes.
You may use a calculator on this paper.

---

1 The pie chart shows the replies to a survey on holiday destinations.

America

Britain

84°

Europe

Other

a 7 people answered 'America'.
How many people were in the survey altogether? _____ people

b A different survey of 20 people were asked if they preferred staying
in Britain or going abroad for their holidays.
9 people said they preferred to stay in Britain.
On a pie chart, what would the angle be for 'Staying in Britain'?

_____ degrees

2 a For each number in the table write a factor of that number that is
between 10 and 20.

Number	Factor between 10 and 20
48	
150	
51	

b Is 150 a multiple of 60? Tick (✓) Yes or No.

Yes ☐   No ☐

Explain how you know.

_____

3 Here are eight number cards.

$$\boxed{-3}\ \boxed{-1}\ \boxed{-1}\ \boxed{0}\ \boxed{2}\ \boxed{6}\ \boxed{8}\ \boxed{9}$$

a What is the range of the numbers? _____

b What is the sum of the numbers? _____

c What is the mode of the numbers? _____

d What is the median of the numbers? _____

e What is the mean of the numbers? _____

4 Here is part of a number grid.

23	24	25	26	27	28
33	34	35	36	37	38
43	44	45	46	47	48

From these numbers, write down one that is:

a a prime number _____

b a square number _____

c Explain why a square number could never be a prime number.

_____

5 a ABC is an isosceles triangle.

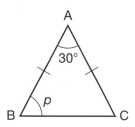

What is angle *p*?

_____ degrees _____
1 mark

b This diagram is not drawn accurately.
Calculate the size of angle *m*.

Show your working.

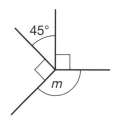

_____ degrees _____
1 mark

6 The triangle *ABC* below is drawn accurately.

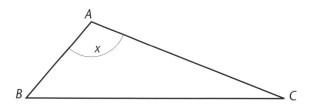

a Measure accurately the angle marked *x*.

_____ degrees _____
1 mark

b The drawing is a scale drawing of a building plot.
The scale is **1 cm represents 50 metres**.
What is the actual length represented by *BC* on the diagram?

_____ metres _____
2 marks

7 A 50p coin has a mass of 8 grams.
How much is one kilogram of 50p coins worth?

£ _____ _____
3 marks

8 The graph shows a straight line.

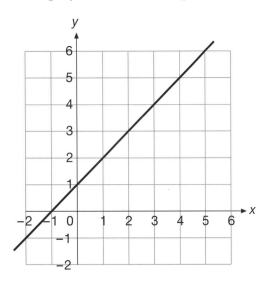

a Fill in the table with some of the points on the line.

(x, y)	(__ , __)	(__ , __)	(__ , __)

2 marks

b Write down the equation of the line. _____

1 mark

c On the graph draw the line $y = x + 3$

1 mark

9 A bicycle wheel has a diameter of 70 cm.

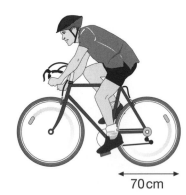

70 cm

a What is the circumference of the wheel?

_____ cm

1 mark

b During a 5 kilometre race, approximately how many times will the wheel turn?

_____ turns

2 marks

10 Use your calculator to work out

$(52 + 25) \times (41 - 19) =$ _____

1 mark

$$\frac{52 + 25}{41 - 19} =$$ _____

1 mark

11 The standard measure for different paper sizes are
A1, A2, A3 etc....
The standard measure for envelopes are C1, C2, C3 etc...
All paper and envelope sizes have the width and height
in the same ratio of approximately 1 : 1.4

Ratio of width to
height is 1 : 1.4

a Work out the height of a piece of A4 paper
that is 21 cm wide.

A4 paper has a height of

 _____ cm

←——21 cm——→

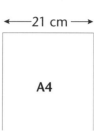

A4

1 mark

b Work out the width of a C5 envelope that is
229 mm high.
Give your answer to the nearest millimetre.

A C5 envelope has a width of

_____ mm

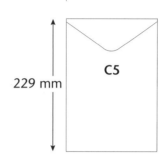

229 mm

C5

1 mark

c Will an A4 piece of paper, when folded in half, fit inside a C5 envelope?
Explain your answer.

_____

_____

1 mark

12 Some information about the capacity of two football grounds is shown in the table.

	Manchester United	Manchester City
Total capacity	67 500	48 000
Percentage of executive seats	3.4%	4.9%

Which club has the most executive seats and by how many?   _____

2 marks

13 Look at this equation.

$3(2x + 13) = 76 + 4x$

Is $x = 18.5$ a solution of this equation? Tick [✓] Yes or No.

Yes ☐   No ☐

Explain your answer.   _____

1 mark

14 Write these expressions as simply as possible.

$7 - 3a + 9 - 7a =$ _____

1 mark

$b^2 + 6b - 2b =$ _____

1 mark

$6c \times 4c =$ _____

1 mark

$\dfrac{12d^3}{3d} =$ _____

1 mark

15 The table shows the number of children in 20 families.

Number of children per family	Frequency
0	2
1	5
2	8
3	4
4	0
5	1

Calculate the mean number of children for the 20 families. _____

2 marks

16 The star is formed using a regular octagon.

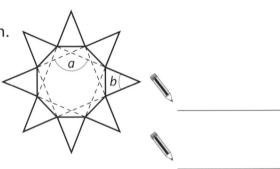

a Work out the value of angle a.

_____ °

1 mark

b Work out the value of angle b.

_____ °

1 mark

17 Construct an angle of 60° at the point A.
Show your construction lines and arcs.

A •_____

2 marks

18 Calculate the length x in the following triangles.
Show your working clearly.
Give your answers to 3 significant figures.

a

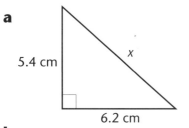

_____ cm _____
2 marks

b

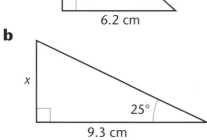

_____ cm _____
2 marks

19 The length of a rectangle is decreased by 10%.
The width of the rectangle is increased by 20%.
By what percentage does the area increase or decrease?

_____ % _____
2 marks

20 What is the nth term of the series
4, 7, 10, 13, 16, ...

_____ _____
2 marks

21 The diagram shows a rectangle inside a right-angled triangle.

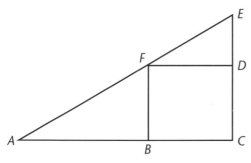

$ED = 4$ cm, $CD = 6$ cm, $EF = 8$ cm.
Find the length AE.

_____ _____
2 marks

Mental Mathematics Test

In your mental mathematics test, you will hear the questions and write your answers on the answer sheets. For the first group of questions you will have 5 seconds to work out each answer and write it down.

Time: 5 seconds

1 Multiply four point three by ten.

1	

2 How many metres are in 300 centimetres?

2		300 cm

3 What is two-fifths of thirty-five?

3	

4 Subtract four from minus six.

4		–6

5 Look at the equation. When x equals six, what is the value of y?

5		$y = x^2 - 5$

6 What is four point five divided by five?

6		4.5

7 To the nearest ten kilometres the length of a motorway is ninety kilometres.

What is the greatest value the length of the motorway could be?

7		km

For the next group of questions you will have 10 seconds to work out each answer and write it down.

Time: 10 seconds

8 The chart shows the number of hours of TV watched by a child in a week.

On which day was 3 hours of TV watched?

8	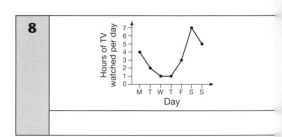

9 A robot moves so that it is always the same distance from a fixed point.

What is the name of the shape of the robot's path?

9	

10 Look at the grid. Write down the coordinates of the mid-point of AB.

10	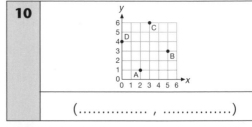

$$(\ldots\ldots\ldots , \ldots\ldots\ldots)$$

11 How many quarters are there in two and a half?

11	

12 Think about the mass two kilograms.

About how many pounds is that?

Circle the best answer on the answer sheet.

12	3 3.5 4 4.5 5

13 Look at the fraction.

Write it in its simplest form.

13		$\dfrac{85}{100}$

14 In a survey one-third of the people asked preferred to go abroad for their holidays.

What percentage is this?

14	

15 What is the area of this rectangle?

<table>
<tr><td>15</td><td></td><td>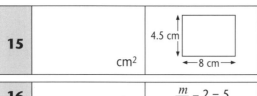</td></tr>
</table>

| 15 | | cm² | 4.5 cm ← 8 cm → |

16 Look at the equation. Solve it to find the value of m.

| 16 | | $\frac{m}{3} - 2 = 5$ |

17 The average weight of a male squirrel is 500 grams.

Female squirrels have an average weight that is 5% less than this.

What is the average weight of a female squirrel?

| 17 | | g |

18 A cardboard box measures half a metre by thirty centimetres by twenty centimetres.

Which of the calculations on the answer sheet will give the volume of the box?

Ring the correct answer.

18	0.5 x 20 x 30
	0.5 x 2 x 3
	0.5 x 0.3 x 0.2
	0.5 + 0.3 + 0.2

19 What is a quarter of two thirds of sixty?

| 19 | |

20 Look at the inequality.

How many integer solutions are there?

| 20 | | $3 \leq n \leq 9$ |

For the next group of questions you will have 15 seconds to work out each answer and write it down.

Time: 15 seconds

21 Write down a factor of 48 that is bigger than ten but less than twenty.

| 21 | |

22 The first odd number is one. What is the hundredth odd number?

| 22 | |

23 On the grid sketch the line $x + y = 4$.

| 23 | *(grid with x and y axes, marked 0 1 2 3 4 5 6)* |

24 What is the area of a circle with a radius of 3 centimetres?

Give your answer in terms of π.

| 24 | | cm² |

25 I can make twenty-four different four-digit numbers from the digits one, two, three and four.

How many of these will be odd numbers?

| 25 | **1 2 3 4** |

26 Look at the calculation.

Write down an approximate answer.

| 26 | | $\dfrac{38.5 \times 51.6}{4.89}$ |

27 Complete the factorisation.

| 27 | $x^2 - 16 = (x + 4)\,(\ldots\ldots\ldots\ldots\ldots)$ |

28 A bag contains only red and blue balls.

There are twice as many blue balls as red balls.

I take a ball at random from the bag.

What is the probability that the ball will be red?

| 28 | |

29 What 3-D shape has four vertices?

| 29 | |

30 What is the product of all the integers from 1 to 5?

| 30 | 1 2 3 4 5 |

Revision checklist

Number

I am able to:

- Multiply and divide decimals ☐
- Add, subtract, multiply and divide negative numbers ☐
- Find a percentage of a quantity ☐
- Find one quantity as a percentage of another ☐
- Find the new value after a percentage increase or decrease ☐
- Find the original amount after a percentage increase or decrease ☐
- Divide a quantity in a given ratio ☐
- Work out powers of numbers ☐
- Round off numbers and give the limits of accuracy ☐
- Write numbers in and calculate with standard form ☐

Algebra

I am able to:

- Simplify algebraic expressions ☐
- Use formulae expressed in words and in symbols ☐
- Factorise simple expressions ☐
- Expand and simplify a pair of linear brackets ☐
- Draw a graph by plotting points ☐
- Recognise graphs of the form $x = y$, $y = b$ and $y = x$; $y = x^2$, $y = x^3$ and $y = \frac{1}{y}$ ☐
- Interpret real-life graphs ☐
- Solve simple equations by rearrangement ☐
- Solve equations where the unknown appears on both sides of the equals sign ☐
- Solve equations involving brackets ☐
- Solve equations using trial and improvement ☐
- Solve a pair of simultaneous equations ☐

Shape, Space and Measures

I am able to:

- Calculate angles from known facts ☐
- Plot and measure bearings ☐

- Describe and draw shapes that have been transformed by enlargement, rotation and reflection ☐
- Calculate the interior and exterior angles of regular polygons ☐
- Recognise the standard 3-D shapes and their nets ☐
- Calculate the perimeter and area of standard shapes ☐
- Calculate the circumference and area of a circle ☐
- Calculate the volume of cuboids ☐
- Use a ruler and compasses to do constructions ☐
- Find the loci of points obeying certain rules ☐
- Use similar triangles to calculate sides of triangles ☐
- Use Pythagoras' theorem to calculate sides of right-angled triangles ☐
- Use trigonometry to calculate sides and angles of right-angled triangles ☐
- Find the length of an arc and area of a sector ☐
- Find angles using the circle theorems ☐

Handling Data

I am able to:

- Draw and interpret pie charts ☐
- Draw and interpret scatter diagrams and lines of best fit ☐
- Design and criticise questions for surveys ☐
- Compare distributions using statistical measures ☐
- Use box plots and cumulative frequency diagrams to find medians and interquartile ranges ☐
- Calculate the probability of an event ☐
- Calculate the probability of a combined event from a sample space diagram ☐
- Calculate the probability of a combined event from a tree diagram ☐